AUDUBON'S ANIMALS

AUDUBON

THE QUA

Audubon

NEW YORK : THE STUDIO PUBLICATIONS, INC. I

S ANIMALS

UPEDS OF NORTH AMERICA

COMPILED & EDITED BY ALICE FORD

SSOCIATION WITH THOMAS Y. CROWELL COMPANY

We gratefully acknowledge the official commen-
dation given this book by the National Audubon
Society, 100 Fifth Avenue, New York, the famous
organization dedicated in the artist's name to the
conservation of wild life and other renewable
natural resources.

FOREWORD

Had not John James Audubon, the most gifted of our early naturalist-artists, been driven by an insatiable curiosity about wild life and an instinctive desire to paint, he would certainly never have created his great monuments—the *Quadrupeds* and the *Birds*.

John James Audubon, mammal painter, a man of courage, emotion and adventure, was impatient with the stereotyped styles of the day and replaced them with a fresh eye and palette. Not content with the usual academic representations of mammal subjects, he went to the far places of new America to find the quadrupeds in their native habitat. His was not the insenate art of a Wilson nor the product of the cabinet artist and skilled copyist. Among the vast array of his paintings are many works of the true genius—paintings which bespeak the man's mastery even more eloquently than did the venerable Elliott Coues when he wrote:

"Vivid and ardent was his genius, matchless he was both with pen and pencil in giving life and spirit to the beautiful objects he delineated with passionate love. . . . Of his work the magical beauties of form and color and movement are all his; his page is redolent with Nature's fragrance."

This historic appraisal was seconded by the great Louis Agassiz who, after examining the first volume of the *Quadrupeds*, affirmed it to be a standard authoritative work without a competitor in America and without equal in Europe.

Undertaking the great task of painting the mammals of North America at a time of life when most men would have paused to rest, Audubon was soon forced to draw heavily on the assistance of friends and of his sons. The Reverend John Bachman, co-author, who put all of the text in its final form, made important original contributions to knowledge, based on long years of study, and his rich experience pervades the text. Also to be noted is the part played by John Woodhouse Audubon, the artist's greatly gifted son, who shouldered immense responsibilities both in the field and at the easel to bring the *Quadrupeds* to fruition. He strove valiantly to fulfill his father's aspirations. Indeed, at times, the paternal inspiration was of measure sufficient to make John Woodhouse Audubon gleam through his father's shadow. See, for example, many of the final plates which John Woodhouse painted following his father's withdrawal in 1846, as well as his tingling description of the dawn call of the Prairie Wolf.

Through research connected with the Audubon Gallery in the American Museum of Natural History, New York, one of the most extensive exhibitions of Audubon originals in the world, I came to know the editor of this book, Alice Ford, as a researcher of tireless energy, who has combined meticulous care with a genuine love for her subject —the great, indefatigable John James Audubon.

Doubtless most persons, examining this work for the first time, will turn first to the pictures, especially those in color, in which Audubon depicted the wonders of nature as he saw them in that new and bountiful land of promise, which then comprised twenty-six states and one million square miles of Indian territory. It was a land with a seemingly limitless abundance of savages, buffalo, wild pigeons, and cathedral forests, seen by many a Sutter, Clark, Boone, boy Lincoln, and—to our everlasting enrichment—an Audubon. However, it would be a serious mistake to pass over the biographical introduction, for there Alice Ford provides this monument with its heart. She has spent several years' research among the letters, journals, drawings, water colors, oil paintings, curios, and personal mementoes of this pioneer artist. There is not a niche of Auduboniana which she has not investigated; and now, with the help of her expert selection, one may gain a true impression of the artist.

This superbly illustrated book with its modern nomenclature eliminates the fiction of nineteenth century mammalogy. Pertinent geographical notes, intermixed with frontier color, comprise valuable contributions not alone to art, but to science and history. The publishers are to be commended for the perfection of the reproduction, and for making the *Quadrupeds* readily available today.

E. THOMAS GILLIARD

American Museum of Natural History
New York

ACKNOWLEDGMENTS

I wish to pay tribute to the memory of the foremost Audubon biographer, Professor Francis Hobart Herrick of Western Reserve University, whose brilliant research extended over nearly half a century until his death in 1940. With Mr. Stanley Clisby Arthur of New Orleans, another outstanding biographer, he is largely responsible for our generation's accurate knowledge of the naturalist.

The American Museum of Natural History, New York, contributed importantly to the completion of this book. Dr. Robert Cushman Murphy's interest is gratefully acknowledged. Mr. T. Donald Carter of the Department of Mammals checked and revised my efforts to provide the present names and ranges of Audubon's quadrupeds, and through his expert knowledge clarified many obscurities regarding the original text of the *Quadrupeds*. Mr. E. Thomas Gilliard of the Department of Birds, Audubon authority and enthusiast, has not only written the foreword of the present work but gave much valuable aid in connection with the museum's extensive Audubon collections. His welcome suggestions with regard to the text are also gratefully acknowledged. Miss Hazel Gay, Librarian, helped with research and expedited procedures. Mr. Thane L. Bierwert, Chief of the Division of Photography, is entitled to special mention for his expert services. Mrs. Martha I. Cotter of the Department of Mammals helped in checking the captions.

Through its active interest, encouragement, and assistance, the National Audubon Society of New York has also been of the utmost assistance, especially Mr. John H. Baker, President, Mr. Kenneth D. Morrison, Editor of *Audubon Magazine* and Director of Public Information for the society, Mr. John K. Terres, Managing Editor, and Mrs. Monica Avery De La Salle, Librarian and Director of Exhibitions, to whom I am more than grateful. Mrs. De La Salle channeled the society's cooperation and helped with research and the location of certain pictures and collectors. Permission to quote from the society's rare George Bird Grinnell Collection of unpublished letters and to examine the original printer's copy of the *Viviparous Quadrupeds of North America* was graciously given. Its several exhibitions in connection with the Centennial Year were inspiring.

Princeton University, which presented the first Audubon Centennial Exhibition on the eve of 1951, and introduced its outstanding collection to the public, not only made its rare letters and manuscripts available but provided a catalogue, transcript, and photographs. For their help and kindness I am deeply grateful to Mr. Howard C. Rice, Jr., Curator of Special Collections in the Firestone Library; Mr. Henry L. Savage, Archivist; and Miss Elizabeth Fitton, Librarian of the Marquand Library of Art.

My appreciation is also expressed to Mr. G. W. Cottrell, Jr., Editor, Harvard University Library, for coordinating matters pertaining to research, and for his direction of Harvard's admirable Centennial Exhibition. Dr. Alfred S. Romer, Director of Harvard's Museum of Comparative Zoology, kindly permitted quotation of a rare letter.

I take great pride in acknowledging the cooperation of The Pierpont Morgan Library in allowing use, by the engravers, of their fine folio edition of the *Quadrupeds* for color plates. To Mr. Frederick B. Adams, Jr., Director, both the publishers and I are most earnestly indebted for his sincere interest and good counsel. Miss Felice Stampfle, Curator of Prints and Drawings, courteously made the library's six water color drawings by J. J. Audubon available for study. Mr. Mark D. Brewer, the library's photographer, made a major contribution to the book through his services in connection with all 156 of the Audubon plates of the *Quadrupeds*. (The library's folio edition and original drawings were purchased fifty-one years ago by Mr. Pierpont Morgan from Mr. Theodore Irwin, noted Oswego bibliophile.)

The American Philosophical Society of Philadelphia, The Club of Odd Volumes, and the Manuscript Division of the New York Public Library granted permission to quote from their Audubon letter collections.

Dr. E. Milby Burton, Director of the Charleston Museum, South Carolina, made an extended loan of a full transcript of the museum's superb collection of the letters to and from Audubon's coeditor, John Bachman, as well as useful books and papers.

The Audubon Memorial Museum of Henderson, Kentucky, provided all necessary information concerning its interesting collections.

The New York Historical Society, New York, put its original quadruped drawings at my disposal for study and reproduction, with Miss Caroline Scoon, of the Department of Paintings, assisting. Mrs. Bella C. Landauer is tendered thanks for permitting use of the woodcut of a scene from the artist's life, in the Historical Society's Landauer Collection.

Among the descendants of Audubon, I am grateful to Mr. and Mrs. Victor Morris Tyler of New Haven and their son Morris Tyler of Woodbridge, Connecticut, for enabling me to study their collections. Mr. John S. Williams, another great-grandson, kindly authorized my study and use of his collection on deposit at Princeton University. Miss Susan Lewis Shaffer and Mr. Frank H. Shaffer, Jr., of Cincinnati, descendants, permitted me to draw upon their collections as required. Edward Harris' descendants, Mrs. R. D. Sappington of Hillsdale, Michigan, and Mrs. C. F. Wolters of Swarthmore, Pennsylvania, have cooperated effectively through enthusiastic correspondence. Mrs. Margaret Mc-Cormick of Staten Island, great-granddaughter of Audubon, also kindly assisted.

Mr. E. J. L. Hallstrom, who purchased from Leonard Audubon of Sydney, Australia, a group of original paintings by the Audubons, which he presented to the National Gallery of Art, Washington, allowed the publishers to have his mammal pictures photographed before shipment to this country.

Mr. Elkan Silberman of the E. and A. Silberman Galleries, New York, authority on the preservation and restoration of paintings, offered expert observations on Audubon's theory with regard to glazing.

Valuable cooperation was given with research, photographs, or both, by the following: The New York Public Library's Rare Book Room, Art and Print Rooms, General History Room, and Webster Branch; the Library of the Academy of Natural Sciences, Philadelphia; the Historical Society of Pennsylvania; the Library Company of Philadelphia; the Wadsworth Atheneum, Hartford; Mr. Henry E. Schnakenberg of Newtown, Connecticut; The Brooklyn Museum; Thomas J. Gannon, Inc., the Edwin Hewitt Gallery, the Ferargil Gallery, the Racquet & Tennis Club, Kennedy & Company, The Macbeth Gallery, and The Old Print Shop, Inc., New York; Goodspeed's Book Shop of Boston; The Boatmen's National Bank of St. Louis; the Public Library of Cincinnati; the Library of Western Reserve University, Cleveland; the Boston Society of Natural History; The Cincinnati Art Museum; The Detroit Institute of Arts; the Massachusetts Historical Society; the Missouri Historical Society; the Philadelphia Museum of Art; the City Art Museum of St. Louis; Charles Sessler, Books and Prints, Philadelphia; the Virginia Museum of Fine Arts; the Southwest Museum, Los Angeles; The Butler Art Institute, Youngstown, Ohio; and Mrs. Richard Graham of New Orleans.

Finally, for steadfastly sharing my belief in the stature and importance of this revival of Audubon's *Quadrupeds*, and for his feats on the production of the book, I shall always be deeply indebted and thankful to Mr. Bryan Holme of The Studio Publications, Inc., who has guided the venture to this most gratifying completion.

ALICE FORD

New York
September, 1951

CONTENTS

AUDUBON AND "THE QUADRUPEDS"

1

REDISCOVERY OF "THE QUADRUPEDS"

One of John James Audubon's earliest memories of childhood was of a clash between a quadruped and a bird. His mother's parrot, Mignonne, was screeching for her breakfast when a large pet monkey, enraged by her abuse, hopped on her perch and throttled it. The little boy, looking on, let out a piercing cry that brought his mother running to the scene. Until the culprit was sentenced to live out his days in chains, and the hapless Mignonne "buried with all the pomp of a cherished lost one," John James was inconsolable. Protagonist and victim in this brief domestic tragedy were the symbols, as fate would have it, of the furred and feathered lodestars of Audubon's career.

January 27, 1951, marked the centennial of the artist's death. To recent generations he has been known as a bird painter—the greatest. But for decades his superb delineations of North American quadrupeds have been neglected. In Nature's design for the Little Short-tailed Shrew and its nocturnal brethren may lie the answer. Unprepossessing of mien even when painted by a master, this four-legged cousin of another small denizen of the animal kingdom, the Hummingbird, cannot compete with the beautiful nectar feeder. Bright and graceful plumage has readier appeal; and yet, if one turns to the far fewer quadrupeds—which, besides being mostly nocturnal, are harder to obtain—their often inexplicable intuitions, habits, and mysterious adaptations prove of absorbing interest. Their sagacity and cunning are more than a match for the outward attractions of the birds, and they are closer to our also viviparous selves in the scale of creation.

The time is ripe for a revival of interest in this heritage. Too long neglected, it is extraordinary in both an artistic and scientific light. All Audubon's animals published between 1845 and 1848 in his monumental, folio-sized work, awe-inspiringly entitled, *The Viviparous Quadrupeds of North America*, are reproduced in these pages. A number of the original water color drawings used as studies for the plates, and other fine examples in pencil and in oil, are also shown. Some of these works are by Audubon's son, John Woodhouse Audubon, who followed what his father referred to as the Audubon method. Five additional pictures by the younger Audubon were lithographed for the small, or octavo, edition first published, complete, in 1854. This miniature version dropped the term "viviparous" (meaning "to produce living young from within the body") in the second edition. The heavy undertaking, conceived, begun, and partly carried through by Audubon, was completed by his sons and his friend, the Reverend John Bachman. Victor Gifford, his eldest son, handled the publishing and subscriptions and also lent a hand with the backgrounds for the pictures. John Woodhouse Audubon, who painted nearly half of the animals for the folio edition, also obtained some of the southwestern specimens. Bachman was coauthor and science editor of the text. The large folio lithographs were printed by J. T. Bowen of Philadelphia and issued at intervals until 1848. Audubon retired in 1846, when a hundred of the one hundred and fifty folio plates were finished and the first volume of the text was ready.

"In our illustrations," Bachman wrote in the foreword, "we have endeavored to place before the public a series of plates which are not only scientifically correct, but interesting to all, from the varied occupations, expressions, and attitudes we have given to the different species, together with the appropriate accessories such as trees, plants and landscapes, etc., with which the figures of the animals are relieved. We have sought to describe those represented, to make our readers acquainted with their habits, geographic distribution and description, and all that we could ascertain of interest about them. . . ."

Audubon's contemporaries declared the *Quadrupeds* unsurpassed. Its acclaim was world-wide. Today, many of these mammals, about which far less was known during the frontier era, have new names and reduced ranges, these being given in the present work. Deforestation and advancing civilization have of course altered the picture since Audubon's day. At least two, the buffalo and sea otter, are all but extinct, and it should also be noted that Mexican species and the dogs would not appear in a modern field guide. But, leaving the purely scientific approach and classification to the guides, Audubon's *Quadrupeds* return in the appropriate form of an art book, which pays initial notice to masterful delineation such as is not to be found elsewhere.

The romance of the painter's life apropos of his *Birds* need not be repeated. His ambition to paint every North American species, his struggle, his eventual triumphs are well known. But Audubon's story deserves retelling in the light of his other masterpieces. From the perspective of his quadrupeds, his career unfolds with new fascination, leaving a fresh impression of his genius.

2

AUDUBON'S YOUTH: FRANCE AND AMERICA

Born April 26, 1785, at Les Cayes, Santo Domingo, now Haiti, Jean Rabin Fougère Audubon, or Jean Jacques Fougère Audubon, was the natural son of the sea-faring merchant and planter, Captain Jean Audubon of France. At the death of his genteel French Creole mother, Mademoiselle Rabin, the captain took the four-year-old boy and his half-sister Rosa, another love child, home to his wife in Couëron near Nantes. After five years the childless Ann Moynet legally adopted her husband's charges.

Although Audubon drew birds and mammals throughout his boyhood, his only extended art instruction was for six months in the Paris atelier of the renowned Jacques Louis David. The restless seventeen-year-old detested the studio's confinement and drawing from lifeless casts instead of from nature. A year later he set out alone for America and his father's estate, Mill Grove,[1] near Philadelphia. There he was free to live his own life, to study nature, to hunt and sketch endlessly, dance the minuet, play the fiddle and flute, skate and fence, pay court to fifteen-year-old Lucy Bakewell on a nearby plantation. Although some years were to pass before their marriage, this English-born girl was to steady and guide his variable career. She dedicated all her energy to fostering his causes, never questioning their nearly visionary nature. The tall ingratiating Frenchman who by his own description had "large dark eyes, aquiline nose, a fine set of teeth, and long luxuriant ringlets" could not have maintained his course without her.

The earliest existing quadruped by Audubon is the life-size crayon drawing shown on page 33, the "Marmotte de Savoye," made during his return visit to France in 1805, at the age of twenty. Many of his Loire Valley birds drawn that year are still in existence, but the marmot picture is the only known survivor among his early quadruped drawings.

His return to America with a young French business partner in 1806; his marriage to Lucy; the shattering business failures in Kentucky; his decision to portray all America's birds more beautifully than the comparative few by Alexander Wilson, who inadvertently fired him with the ambition; all these events are history. The birds are blamed for most of his early disappointments and business reverses, just as they are credited with the eminence he won. Certainly in his Henderson days they drew him into the Kentucky forests and away from his shopkeeping ledgers toward financial ruin, and momentarily into the hands of an angry mob led by his creditors. But those creatures that "creepeth upon the earth" are partly responsible for his gains and reverses. In his autobiography, *Myself*, he relates how he went on drawing both mammals and birds in those awful hours, stressing that such troubles did their share of good by heightening his creative powers and sensitivities.

One August day in 1812 while Audubon sat sketching the figure of an otter, his brother-in-law Thomas Bakewell appeared with the distressing news that their commercial partnership had foundered. His means were all but swept away by this collapse, and he and Lucy and their infants were made to suffer, yet Audubon turned to his crayons, birds, and mammals with more intensity than ever. In the Kentucky years, Audubon lost two daughters, one in infancy and the other in early childhood.

Tragedy repeated itself at the frontier with quadruped as villain once more and bird as victim. This

---

[1] Now a memorial.

time the horror was far more poignant than with Mignonne and the monkey. Indeed the rumor of it spread so widely that it came to be dramatized in a Japanese print, reproduced on page 33. The artist told in his *Ornithological Biography* of the devastation of his portfolio of bird drawings by Norway Rats, voracious pests, which he later faithfully painted without a trace of the loathing he must have borne them: "An accident which happened to two hundred of my original drawings nearly put a stop to my research in ornithology. I left the village of Henderson in Kentucky to proceed to Philadelphia on business. I looked to all my drawings before my departure, placed them carefully in a wooden box, and gave them to a relative with injunctions to see that no injury should happen to them. When I returned I inquired after my box . . . my treasure. The box was produced and opened. Reader, feel for me—a pair of Norway Rats had taken possession, and had reared a young family amongst the gnawed bits of paper, which, but a few months before, represented nearly a thousand inhabitants of the air! The burning heat which instantly rushed through my brain was too great to be endured. I slept not for several nights, and the days passed like days of oblivion." Finally overcoming his grief, he again took up his gun, notebook, and pencils, with a fresh resolve to turn out "much better drawings than before." But nearly three years were required for him to fill his portfolio again.

After his departure from Kentucky, Audubon went to work as a taxidermist for a private museum in Cincinnati. This was in 1819—the beginning of five most crucial, seeking years. To the distinguished Dr. Samuel L. Mitchell of New York he was indebted for the knowledge which made this urgently needed employment possible. In France years before, Dr. Charles Daubigny, noted naturalist and his father's personal physician, taught him how to catalogue collections. But he was never to excel at taxidermy or the exacting details of science, nor indeed at anything that called for more of unimaginative and unrelieved drudgery than of sheer artistic fire and inspiration. That is why he is regarded as a naturalist in a limited sense only, as genuine ornithologist and zoologist never, but as an artist of unchallenged genius, first and last. And that is why, despite the petty whispering cam-

paigns against the authenticity of his art, beginning in his day, he has been without peer in his field by popular decree for more than a century— "Audubon's epoch," as the eminent Elliott Coues called it. Bachman once wrote about Aububon's industry, his painstaking measurements, meticulous examination and retouching, careful note-taking and voluminous memoranda.

His journal reports that he drew quadrupeds as well as birds, snakes, and human heads during his flatboat journey down the Mississippi in 1820 with young Joseph Mason, botanist and artist assistant, and a gentleman of fortune named Captain Samuel Cummings, whose own aversion to the Norway Rat is humorously described by Audubon in connection with Fig. 140, see page 211.

Long before he met the itinerant painter John Stein in Natchez and received his first instruction in oils, the artist had experimented independently with the medium. The fact that he chose the otter for his first effort under Stein's instruction, copying one of his water color versions, is of striking interest. He told in his own life history how he had often painted the entrapped otter in his Pennsylvania and Kentucky years. Until he began the *Quadrupeds* he called this his favorite subject, and he was to paint it again and again in oils. It is illustrated on page 108. His first tutored attempt proved discouraging. Only in crayon, black chalk, and water color did he display or experience conscious mastery, and he continued throughout his life to deprecate his handling of oil on canvas.

Like much of Audubon's work his success varied. His early birds, though full of promise, were not posed in the intricate or dramatic compositions of his later sophistication, characteristic of his better known water colors and crayons. So it is with his oils, which also vary. The writer of the foreword of the present work, E. Thomas Gilliard, believes his oils, for instance, of the Carolina Paroquet, Bald Eagle, Ruffed Grouse, Pileated Woodpecker, no less than superb, and the more interesting for being entirely by Audubon even as to backgrounds. He adds that some of the inferior oils on mill board fell short because of the enormous pressure under which the artist labored. Two years after his brief course with Stein he received a few free lessons from Thomas Sully, the famous American master, in the technique of oil painting.

3

THE MIDDLE YEARS: ENGLAND AND SCOTLAND

A succession of rebuffs from envious artists and resentful scientists failed to halt Audubon's progress. With Lucy's savings as a tutor on plantations and the sum that he himself had scraped together, he sailed for England on the *Delos* in 1826. His object was to find subscribers and a suitable engraver for the *Birds*. His journal describes the trials and joys of those eventful years, often darkened by moods of longing for the American wilderness, his "beloved birds," Lucy and their sons. Not for some years was his family to join him in England and Scotland. He did not return to them until 1829, after his success was certain.

During his absence he continually tried to superintend the artistic training of his sons by letter, almost as if he foresaw the vital roles they were to play in furthering his publications. To Victor, then seventeen, he wrote: "Let me request you to pay great attention to *drawing* in my style." In the same letter, published by the Club of Odd Volumes, he urged fourteen-year-old John to "draw from nature" and to save every example no matter how indifferent.

The "Otter in a Trap" was his first exercise in England, though in his journal he wrote that it was the sooty little sparrows in the streets of Liverpool that persuaded him to go out and buy brushes. He wished to present the otter painting to the wife of one of his new and sympathetic friends, William Roscoe.

Quadrupeds continued to receive their share of attention while he showed his portfolios of birds to all and sundry. While visiting a relative of his most devoted British friends, the Rathbones, he was called on to show his virtuosity with charcoal. Seated in a drawing room and agreeably surrounded by the ladies after tea, Audubon sketched a dog, then rubbed the drawing with a cork to show what he could do.

In Edinburgh a few weeks later he began rising at dawn to paint the otter again, to try to dispel an extreme feeling of despondency. One Sunday, William Home Lizars, the man who was to engrave the first ten plates of the *Birds*, dropped in after church with his wife for a social visit. The couple praised the otter in the highest terms, saying that they preferred it to the turkey. This was no faint praise, because the aquatint of the Wild Turkey is perhaps his most popular print today, as well as the most valued. His oil and water color versions are among his masterpieces. Later in the day another friend called, and it was the speed of the otter's execution that most impressed him. "No man in either England or Scotland could paint that picture in so short a time," the journal quotes him. Much encouraged by all this praise, Audubon nevertheless attributed it to the fact that his British friends were unfamiliar with his style.

Next day he returned to the otter more earnestly than ever, and after putting the final touches to it he wrote in his journal: "I have been just thirteen hours at it, and had I labored for thirteen weeks I do not think I should have bettered it." He supervised its hanging in the Scottish Academy's exhibition, then had a look around at other pictures. His eyes lingered on a large work by the Flemish master, Frans Snyders (1579–1657), known especially for animal paintings. The subject, "Bear Attacked by Dogs," was not handled precisely to Audubon's liking, although anyone familiar with this overpowering scene may marvel at the audacity of his criticism. He conceded that Rubens' one-time assistant was an expert colorist and a master at finishing the surface, but to him the bear was not a real bear at all and the dogs were "badly drawn, distorted caricatures." "I am sure," his journal concludes, "Snyders did not draw from specimens put in real postures in my way." Never had he himself tackled anything half so ambitious, it should be noted!

Daniel Lizars, father of the engraver and for a time Audubon's agent, commissioned him to paint two fighting cats. "I at once put them in a fighting attitude . . . I painted all day—that is, during all the time I could see." The painting of "two cats fighting like devils over a dead squirrel" took ten hours of rapid, intensive work. Audubon thought well of the draftsmanship but not so much of the finish, or surface. He was often to make this criticism of his oils, both in letters to Lucy and in his journal. But never anywhere did he hint that he might have an equal in the art of animation in the water color drawing of animals from nature. The Audubon Memorial Museum in Henderson, Kentucky, has two striking examples of cat pictures by the Audubons, one by the father, a cat stalking a bird, in water color, and an oil by John, a cat stalking a butterfly.

Sir William Jardine and Prideaux John Selby, ornithologists, asked the visitor from America to teach them his method of drawing squirrels. He played host to them in his rooms. "I showed these gentlemen how I set up my specimens, squared my paper, and soon had them at work drawing a squirrel. They called this a lesson. It was to me like a dream that I, merely a woodsman, should teach men so much my superiors. They worked very well indeed, although I perceived at once that Mr. Selby was more enthusiastic. He exclaimed, 'I will paint all our quadrupeds for my house.' They both remained with me until we could see no more." Sir William brought him the news that night that he had been elected a member of the Edinburgh Society of Arts.

The Snyders bear and dogs in combat had left their mark. Audubon said, however, that it was a gift of three beautiful pheasants that inspired him to begin a painting of these birds attacked by a fox, for an approaching exhibition in London. On the second day of work he complained of having to grind his colors, a task that he detested. By Christmas Eve and Day, 1826, the oil was taking up all the short hours of daylight, his steady painting bringing more weariness than he had ever known. Early on New Year's Day the Countess of Morton sent him four pheasants and a basket of rare hothouse flowers for the completion of the massive oil which, as he began to realize, was a milestone in his career. Now he was not only combining birds and a quadruped pretentiously, but in a medium that challenged and overawed him. This canvas was apparently the forerunner of his handsome "Spaniel Surprising Pheasants," which he himself referred to as "Sauve Qui Peut," meaning "Devil Take the Hindmost," three identical versions of which are owned in this country, one in water color and the two in oil shown on page 34.

It is interesting to follow his philosophy as he proceeded: "I keep at my painting closely, have labored hard, but my work is bad; some inward feeling tells me when it is good. No one, I think, paints in my method. I, who have never studied but by piece-meal, form my pictures according to my ways of study. I am now working on a Fox. I take one neatly killed, put him up on wires, and when satisfied of the truth of my position, I take my palette and work as rapidly as possible; the same with my birds. If practicable, I finish the bird at one sitting—often, it is true, of fourteen hours—so that I think they are correct both in detail and composition."

One day his work was interrupted by the arrival of a gift of a book by the great wood engraver, Thomas Bewick. Audubon had already seen and avidly studied his notable *History of British Birds*; now he was to do the same with Bewick's *General History of the Quadrupeds*. He became well acquainted with the aged illustrator and artist.

He reached the point where he must decide on a foreground for his "Fox and Pheasants," so he set out in the gray daylight with a coal porter and his cart to fetch stones for it. He returned with a supply and worked at them all the morning.

That afternoon he visited an exhibition. This time an animal painting by the famous Hondecoeter caught his eye. Melchior d'Hondecoeter (c. 1636–1695) was a Dutch painter of animals, particularly of fowls. The oil did not come up to his standards: "The animals seemed to me to be drawn from poorly stuffed specimens, but the coloring, the finish, the manner, the effect, were most beautiful, and but for the lack of Nature in the animals the picture commanded admiration and attention."

The more and more frequent allusions to his own lack of *finish*, as compared with that of Snyders' and Hondecoeter's oils, were made, almost invariably, with confidence in his superior mastery of animation, the art of creating a realistic and live rather than statuesque effect. He was quick to detect and criticize a lack of firsthand knowledge of wild life in the paintings of the masters. But he was equally candid about his own shortcomings: "My painting," he said of "Fox and Pheasants" in his journal, "has now arrived at the difficult point. To finish highly without destroying the general effect, or to give the general effect and care not about the finishing? I am quite puzzled. Sometimes I like the picture then a heat rises to my face and I think it a miserable daub. This is the largest piece I have ever done. As to the birds, I am quite satisfied, but the ground, the foliage, the sky, the distance are dreadful."

Nevertheless, by morning, while longing for the arrival of a promised white pheasant that he needed for a "keystone of light," he was again ready to attack the canvas. He worked steadily for five hours and then only left it because he had to—to read a paper on the alligator's habits before a University of Liverpool assemblage. As for the white pheasant, it never arrived, and its place was taken in the scene by a black crow.

At the close of the Scottish Academy exhibition his "Otter" was returned to him. On January 23 he mused in his journal: "I have powerfully in my mind to give my picture of the 'Trapped Otter' to Mr. Basil Hall,[2] and by Washington, I will. No one deserves it more." In the end it seems that this oil went to his intimate friends the Rathbones, who kept it in their home for many years. Only when it was decided to present the painting to a Liverpool public collection did Mrs. Rathbone admit to the family that the otter's plight had always filled her with horror. But the realism of the scene was part of the reason for Audubon's pride in it.

As the days lengthened he often remained at his easel from eight till four in the afternoon. "A man may do a good deal," his journal reflects, "provided he has the power of laying the true tints at once, and does not muddy his colors or need glazing afterwards. Now a query arises. Did the ancient artists and colorists ever glaze their work? I sometimes think they did not, and I am inclined to think thus because their work is of great strength of standing, and extremely solid and confirmed on the canvas—a proof to me that they painted clean and bright at once, but that this *once* they repeated, perhaps, as often as three times. Glazing certainly is a beautiful way of effecting transparency, particularly over shadowy parts; but I frequently fear, the coating being so thick, that time preys on these parts more powerfully than on those unglazed, so that the work is sooner destroyed by its application than without it. I am confident Sir Joshua Reynolds' pictures fade so much in consequence of his constant glazing." Audubon, comparatively unschooled, did not realize that the opposite was true, and that glazing had been in use primarily as a preservative for hundreds of years before his doubts arose. Titian, who like others of the Renaissance was a noble exponent of *finish*, employed a mixture of oil and glaze for finishing the surface. It might have served Audubon well to know this, and to have realized that no glaze was ever to be added until the canvas was thoroughly and absolutely dry, some little time after the work was completed.

About this time he was introduced to the *camera lucida*, an enormous timesaver for artists. This solid, portable sheet of prismatic glass could be set up to enable the artist, while looking through an eyepiece, to outline objects exactly and swiftly as if by tracing. In the years ahead young John would use it to accelerate the copying of figures from the folios for the small editions of both birds and mammals.

Audubon continued to study his own painting and the work of others critically. The spectacle of his large and magnificent "Black Cocks" exhibited on the wall of the Royal Institution left him somewhat in awe of his daring in having painted these birds in numbers—grandly—against a big landscape and with a foreground, and, above all, in oils. He turned from the picture to look at a work by Edwin Henry Landseer. The English artist, a newly elected

---

[2] Captain Hall's books on his foreign travels were then the vogue. He was about to visit America and write another, carrying various letters of introduction from Audubon to several persons here.

associate of the Royal Academy and then only twenty-four, was regarded as a most promising animal painter. His "Fighting Dogs" had attracted considerable attention in 1819, with predictions of his renown. But his portrayal of "The Death of a Stag" impressed Audubon as wanting in several highly important ways: "Nature was not there, although a Stag, three dogs, and a Highlander were introduced on the canvas. The Stag had his tongue out and his mouth shut! The principal dog, a greyhound, held the Deer by one horn very prettily, and, in the attitude of a ballet dancer, was about to cast the noose over the head of the animal. To me such a picture is quite a farce; not so here, however." Again his appraisal was far too harsh.

His growing interest in trying his hand at ambitious oils combining quadruped and bird in elaborate compositions was interrupted by a practical event of utmost importance. In March 1827 the first of the folio *Birds* began to come from the engraver, to continue in lovely succession until 1838. By summer a desperate lack of funds returned him to his ever popular "Otter"; he made seven identical copies to sell in London, Liverpool, and Manchester, often taking them fresh from the easel to some street of dealers. Characteristically, he bought a five-key flageolet for Victor with part of his earnings. He sold an uncertain number of copies of the "Otter" and other oils to defray his expenses in 1828—almost to the point where his quadrupeds may be said to have supported him to the advantage of his *Birds*.

His friend William Gregg, about to deliver a lecture on the duck-billed platypus of Australia, asked him to make sketches of all the parts of that curious birdlike mammal.

He could not advise his sons too firmly to devote themselves to art, and to conquer the oil medium which continued to evade him. Speaking of John he exhorted Lucy: "I do most particularly beg of you to urge him and to tell him all this from me," adding that the boys should learn to draw as well as he did in order to help him complete his collection of drawings. He instructed that John should skin and ship him all kinds of birds, mosses, leaves, and lichen-covered branches for painting habitats.

John Audubon, though he was abler at field work and a more enterprising artist than his older brother, was livelier and harder to rear than quiet, mannerly Victor, the Bakewells' favorite and the likelier prospect for conducting his father's business. John preferred oil in the end; and he painted many mammals on canvas. Audubon's often deeply discouraged letters to Lucy about this technique must have impressed his sons: "I am perfectly confident that the delineations are correct to perfection, [but] I am likely to abandon this style forever . . . with considerable regret. I will think frequently how hard it is for me not to have another life to spend, to acquire a talent that needs a whole life to reach to any moderate degree of perfection." The Club of Odd Volumes published several such letters in a limited edition.

Often in the winter of 1828 he visited a small London menagerie—Cross's exhibition of quadrupeds and live birds—which afforded him a rare release because there he could look upon nature even if, as he said, it was caged. Mr. Cross honored him with a lifetime ticket of admission. He also regularly visited the Zoological Gardens, which were to figure importantly nearly twenty years later in the completion of the *Quadrupeds*. "The Zoological Gardens improve daily," his journal relates. "They are now building winter quarters for the animals there. The specimens of skins from all parts of the world which are presented there are wonderful, but they have no place for them." He particularly admired two large and handsome beavers.

Before Audubon had left the United States he had painted a water color of an eagle seizing a lamb. In London during the summer of 1828, between sessions of directing the coloring of his *Birds*, he began to render the subject in oils. "I am sure the positions of the bird and his prey are wholly correct," he wrote in his journal. But again he realized that such experiments in oil would not increase subscriptions to his *Birds*. "Eagle and Lamb," "Otter in a Trap," and a popular oil of "Rabbits," which he had repeated, had to be set aside while he went to the Continent on business.

On September 1, 1828, he crossed the channel to seek subscribers in his boyhood France. Though the rewards were scarcely equal to the effort, this journey had its compensations. He enjoyed the theater and attended regularly, as he had done in England and Scotland; and he spoke excitedly of his visits with the celebrities of the day. He had an interview with Gérard who had studied with his teacher, Jacques Louis David. Redouté, incomparable painter of flowers, presented him with a copy of his "Les Roses." Constant, the noted engraver, and the Duc d'Orléans also received him. And while he was in Paris he went to the Louvre where he examined closely the most celebrated pictures of animals, birds, fruits, and flowers, painted by the great masters.

He returned to London early in November. The following month he completed the "Eagle and Lamb," as well as one of his two large oils of the "Spaniel and Pheasants." His good friend the portrait painter, Sir Thomas Lawrence, who had been helping him find a market for such canvasses, called the former a fine picture. But he puzzled Audubon, when, after studying the far handsomer dog and pheasants from every angle, he made no comment at all. Turning to the "Otter" he pronounced it very fine—the invariable reaction.

When Audubon returned to America in March 1829, he received the recognition long due him from his countrymen. He met a Swiss painter, George Lehman, who was to paint landscapes for some of his Southern birds, in a capacity similar to that of Joseph Mason who painted habitats for some of the *Birds* and who taught Audubon the use of botanical effects. These two men contributed as much to the backgrounds of the *Birds* as Victor Audubon did to some of the backgrounds of *The Viviparous Quadrupeds of North America*.

Another purpose of his trip to America was to complete some of his previous pictures and do additional ones.

4

FRIENDSHIP WITH BACHMAN

His mission to America completed, Audubon returned to England with Lucy on New Year's Day, 1831, taking with him many new pictures for his engraver, R. Havell. But before many months, he decided to return to the United States in search of birds, and by October he was on an expedition to the South, with Mason and Lehman as assistants. On October 23, he wrote to Lucy concerning an event of the utmost significance, not only in connection with his bird project but, even more so, with respect to the coming *Quadrupeds*: "I found a man [Reverend John Gilman] of learning and sound heart, willing to lend 'the American Woodsman' a hand. He walked with me and had already contrived to procure us cheaper lodgings, when lo, he presented me in the street to the Reverend Mr. Bachman!!—Mr. Bachman!! Why my Lucy, Mr. Bachman would have us all to stay at his house . . . He would not suffer us to proceed farther south for three weeks. He looked as if his heart had been purposely made of the most benevolent materials granted to man by the Creator . . . Could I have refused his kind invitation? . . . Out shooting every day—skinning, drawing, talking ornithology the whole evening, noon and morning. This, Dearest Friend, is the situation of Thy Husband in Charleston, South Carolina." This is but one of the letters in the magnificent collection of the American Philosophical Society.

Before he bade his host good-by weeks later, he knew that he had made not only a fast friend but a real ally, as agile as himself with trap and gun, and more than equal to the trust of serving as his American agent for the *Birds*. Bachman called him the "Nestor of American ornithology," and welcomed their association. Audubon could not have imagined what else would arise from this alliance besides Bachman's help with the Southern birds: his far more telling influence on the *Quadrupeds*, and the marriage of his eldest daughters to the Audubon sons.

Bachman's qualifications as adviser and agent were impressive. Of German and Swiss descent, this native of Rhinebeck, New York, who was five years Audubon's junior, had loved the study of nature from boyhood. He had known intimately the "father of American ornithology," Scottish-born Alexander Wilson, whose bird paintings had challenged Audubon. He was proud also of having known the illustrious Alexander von Humboldt, German scientist. Tuberculosis caused his removal to the South in his young manhood, where he became a prominent member of the Lutheran clergy. His study of wild life and his unremitting research were an added career, never a mere hobby, and his reputation as a naturalist became world-wide. In 1838, close to the beginning of the work on the *Quadrupeds*, he addressed the Zoological Department of the Society of Naturalists and Physicians of Germany, in Freiburg, on "The Present State of Natural Science in the United States."

The Bachman home was known for its hospitality. Audubon and his sons, his assistants, and sometimes his wife, were guests off and on for years. To make room for the constant stream of visitors—often men of science—the smaller children were sometimes billeted in the halls!

Despite the sad accounts of the dying that befell this very large family—to be read in the Charleston Museum's remarkable Bachman letter collection—one gains the impression that here was a happy, ebullient household. The study, where Audubon and his friend spent hour upon hour, was lined with books and stuffed and bottled specimens. From their desks they could stroll out on a broad piazza that overlooked the garden, which Bachman's wizardry at coaxing rare blooms to luxuriance had made a fragrant sea of poetically named flowers—jessamine, roses, cloth-of-gold, and countless others. The paneled drawing room's ceiling of stuccoed garlands, its stately mantels, formal mirrors, Adam sofa, Dresden figurines, Bohemian glass, crystal chandeliers, all reflected the dignity of the man who was to influence Audubon more than any other from the day of their meeting. By spring the artist wrote Lucy that Bachman was "worth a gold mine" to him.

The two men agreed that Victor was the logical selection for the all-important handling of subscriptions. In behalf of both the *Birds* and *Quadrupeds* he was to prove himself worthy of all the faith they entrusted. While Audubon and John were exploring the Florida coast for birds in 1832, and Labrador in 1833, Victor was attending to the publications in England.

In 1833 the artist wrote to Victor: "John has drawn a few birds as good as any I ever made." As for John's own impression of his progress, this point is charmingly made in this unpublished letter [3] to Victor, dated Charleston, November 5, 1833: "My Dear Brother: At what a rate we are whirled in this world of ours, and how little we know what may befall us—that I who's head was full of Steamboats and sail boats and cash accounts should go to painting and drawing 'Birds of America.' I am working that I may some day become a Second Audubon—

not to make a fortune. My wish is that I may some day publish some birds or quadrupeds and that my name may stand as does my Father's . . . I have drawn several birds for publication that at least are well done, and I hope to rattle them off as fast as my Father in another year . . . but I may yet die a poor devil in the back woods of Kentucky. I can hardly believe I am twenty-one. I have left off many of my Kentuc' expressions and they are forgotten like our past troubles." John referred to his experience as a clerk in Louisville with his uncle, Nicholas Berthoud, and to his clerical job on a Mississippi steamboat. The latter was shortlived and might have been even shorter had it not been for his personal charm and excellent fiddling, which made his employers overlook his errors. His mother had persuaded him to return to his painting and to gathering specimens for his father who continued to plead for his assistance.

By 1834 the family was united in England. Audubon's letters to Bachman spoke proudly of John's and Victor's attainments. They had toured Europe, become fluent linguists and admirable musicians, and were by this time altogether young gentlemen. More important, they were making rapid strides at painting—John at black chalk and oil portraits, and Victor at battle scenes and landscapes. John sometimes had five sitters in a day; and yet he was managing to draw and paint from nature, and to copy the old masters for his ready customers. He could earn a creditable living, Audubon hinted in a letter to Bachman by way of encouraging the boy's engagement to Maria Rebecca, Bachman's eldest daughter. This praise was having its effect, if one is to judge by the humorous remarks to his friend, written shortly afterward: "Our Dear Child Maria has written fifty-two letters to my Dear Boy John. Her father, the Reverend John Bachman, has written seven letters to his friend J.J.A. in the meantime. Only think of the disparity between lovers of the one sort and those who call themselves Lovers of Science." [4]

---

[3] American Philosophical Society.

[4] Club of Odd Volumes.

5

AUDUBON BEGINS "THE QUADRUPEDS"

John and Victor became Audubon's assistants in 1836. The next year saw John and Maria married and settled in London. But an equally momentous event took place in Charleston about the time of their wedding, with Audubon's announcement to the family that he would begin work on the *Quadrupeds* the moment the *Birds* and *Ornithological Biography* were finished. Bachman heartily approved of this decision.

In 1839 the Audubons returned to America to live. They took a house in White Street in New York. The miniature edition of the *Birds* absorbed them, but plans for the *Quadrupeds* were earnestly begun with the issuing of a Prospectus. Bachman, feeling closer to the Audubon family fortunes than ever because of his Mary Eliza's recent marriage to Victor, did not hesitate to express disapproval of the premature announcement. He warned Audubon in September 1839 that he was moving "too fast" and without enough examples to show to subscribers. "It must be no half-way affair," he wrote. "You will be bothered with the wolves and foxes. The Western Deer are no joke, and the ever-varying Squirrels were sent, I fear, by the Old Boy himself to puzzle naturalists . . . Say in what manner I can assist you." Speaking of their new grandchild, he closed with another characteristic flash of humor: "I'm told Maria's Lucy has a will of her own. She must have inherited it from the John Bull and Johnny Crapeau mixture—not from the Germans. It is a pity that the grumbling Englishman and the excitable Frenchman should spoil the blood of so many good children."

Before the end of 1839 Bachman had been drafted in earnest, and he conceded: "You cannot do without me in this business." [5] A few days later he was adding with spirit: "We will talk when we meet again. We are done with the Birds, but in the Quadrupeds I will show you trap, my boy. Just bring along with you Harlan, Peale, Ord and the other Bipeds and Quadrupeds, and I will row you all up salt river together. I can show the whole concern that they have often been barking with cold noses on the back track. About this partnership in the *Quadrupeds*, we will talk more about it when we meet. I am not ashamed to let my name stand along with yours, and I believe too that it may aid the sale of the work, which, next to its being well got up, is all I can care about. I am also anxious to do something for the benefit of John and Victor, which, alas, in addition to the treasures they have already, is all I can do for them whilst my head is warm. The expenses and the profits will be yours. In due time it will sell as well as the Birds, and if the boys with their good points and industry cannot be independent after all this—they deserve to starve." Bachman need not have worried. He closed with this advice: "Employ yourself in drawing every quadruped you can lay your hands on. If you can possibly get a living ermine—they are common in New York—buy it . . . Don't flatter yourself that this book is child's play—the birds are a mere trifle compared with this. I have been at it all my life . . . but we all have much to learn in this matter. The skulls and teeth must be studied, and color is as variable as the wind—down, down in the earth they grovel, and in digging and

---

[5] Charleston Museum Collection.

studying we grow giddy and cross. Such works as Godman's and Harlan's could be got up in a month, but I would almost as soon stick my name to a forged bank note as to such a mess of *soup-maigre*." [6]

Audubon replied he would be glad to see their names together. He promised to "give the very best figures of all our quadrupeds that ever have been thought or expected," along with "the greatest amount of Truths," thanks to Bachman's aid. "My hair is gray and I am growing old," he said in this Club of Odd Volumes letter, "but what of this—my spirits are as enthusiastical as ever."

Recognizing in John, his son, "stuff enough to make an eminent painter bye and bye," as he told Bachman, he counted on his help with the animal figures. Victor was to create some of the backgrounds, while concentrating on the business. Bachman continued to suggest, admonish, and assist from afar. But this Audubon-Bachman double union was destined to end in sorrow, which was already near at hand. On September 23, 1840, twenty-three-year-old Maria died of tuberculosis, leaving two children. Victor's "Rosy," as Mary Eliza was called, died on May 25, 1841, and on that day Audubon gave vent to his overwhelming grief at the loss of this favorite in a note on the back of a water color painting on which he was working, and which he evidently finished on the twenty-ninth of August. It is quoted on page 49, beneath the figure of a young Cottontail Rabbit, from the Pierpont Morgan Library. Both Audubon sons remarried but remained close to Bachman throughout their lives.

"I am now as anxious about the publication of the *Quadrupeds* as I ever was in the procuring of our Birds—indeed my present interest in Zoology is altogether bent toward the completion of this department of natural science," he wrote Spencer F. Baird in July 1841. Baird, a fifteen-year-old amateur naturalist of unusual promise, had written him letters of admiration from Carlisle, Pennsylvania, which led to a close and mutually helpful friendship. Baird was destined to become one of America's leading scientists, secretary of the Smithsonian Institution, and a founder of the United States National Museum and Bureau of Fisheries. Audubon added that he was "now constantly engaged at drawing the Quadrupeds of our country . . . from daylight every day. Do you pay attention to the quadrupeds around you? If not, I wish you would!" he be-

seeched the boy. "You have *Bats, Wood Rats, Mice, Weasels,* etc. Could you not save all you come across, place them in *common good rum,* and forward them to me?" [7]

The artist's broad assertions to Baird cannot be laid to his alleged fondness for exaggeration. In August he informed a Long Islander, W. O. Ayres, that he had already drawn about one hundred figures, including thirty-six species for the *Quadrupeds.* He urged Ayres to send him some rodents.

Of a large group of bats that came to light in research for this book, only one had ever been published—that one, unimpressively, fully a century ago. The bats have been a mystery. Those of 1846, signed and dated, may well be Audubon's last paintings, due to his failing health—left out because some species remained unfigured?

In the midst of all his feverish activity he found time that summer to buy forty acres at Carmansville (now Washington Heights, 155th Street, New York), and to begin building Minnie's Land, "Minnie" for mother, having been the name given Lucy by the boys when they lived in Scotland. By spring, 1842, his large family which now included Caroline Hall, John's second wife, moved into the roomy mansion, where Victor was soon to bring his English bride, Georgianna Mallory. The estate called for numerous servants and groundsmen. John directed the poultry yards and gardens, painting between times; Victor painted a bit but kept mainly to the publications, while Audubon worked steadily in his barn studio on a knoll. On this very land, two generations earlier, Washington had battled.

Parke Godwin, author and historian, visited the artist at this happy, deeply absorbed point in his crowded career. On a spring day in 1842 he saw him at work on the life-size water colors of the small mammals, the first of the *Quadrupeds.* Godwin called them "masterpieces in their way, surpassing, if that be possible, in fidelity and brilliancy, all that he has done." Returning for a second visit that summer, Godwin was delighted to see fawns and an elk roaming the grounds, oblivious to the barking of the dogs and the cackling and fuss of the turkeys, geese, ducks, and chickens running about everywhere.

Audubon, his eyes keen and deep set as an eagle's, his step light as a deer's, greeted his visitor warmly. Now his white hair hung in ringlets to his shoulders as in his youth. It was kind of Godwin to come, he

[6] Charleston Museum Collection.

[7] Dall, W. H. S. F. Baird.

said, and wise to forsake the city for his own fields and woods. A partly finished sketch of a beaver rested on an easel, and a panther skin lay in one corner. Antlers hung on the walls, and stuffed birds were everywhere. Superb drawings of field mice and birds lay on a long work table crowded with brushes, colors, paper, and aquatints.

The first lithographs of the *Quadrupeds* were now coming from Bowen's press in Philadelphia. The completion of the first plates in the first number in 1842 increased Audubon's anxiety to be off to the Rockies, or at least as far as the Yellowstone river. He wanted new animals to figure. Lucy was uneasy, perhaps even unwilling, to see him undertake this rigorous journey at his advancing age of fifty-seven. But Bachman had been agreeing for several years that the expedition was indispensable to the *Quad-*

rupeds. Edward Harris, Audubon's lifelong friend and early benefactor, was also eager to go along. The plan was for Victor and John to remain in New York, manage Minnie's Land, keep up their share of the painting and attend to the publications.

After a short subscription tour of Canada, Audubon began preparing for his departure. At first the Canadian tour, undertaken to raise urgently needed funds, had been none too promising, though it turned out well in the end. At one stage, he wrote in his journal: "Now I should like to know when, notwithstanding the thousand and one disappointments I meet in this Life, have I felt cast down for more than a few moments. When the rats destroyed my Drawings at Henderson is an exception, and the losing of my own sweet little daughters and daughters-in-law are exceptions."

6

UPPER MISSOURI RIVER EXPEDITION

Not until 1897 were Audubon's picturesque records of his last expedition made available to the public, after having lain forgotten in a drawer for half a century. Why this remarkable adventure has been overlooked by the fictionalized biographies may be explained by the fact that so eventful a story could not be fully told in a few hundred pages. Fortunate it is that Audubon himself wrote prolifically and vividly of all he saw. His Missouri river journal, kept throughout his travels, and some heretofore unpublished letters, enable us to follow his final and most spectacular undertaking.

Journey to St. Louis

On March 11, 1843, the day of his departure, Victor accompanied him as far as Philadelphia. There Audubon was joined by his old friend Harris; and Harris's friend, Lewis Squires, who was to act as expedition secretary; by Isaac Sprague of Wellesley Hills, Massachusetts; and John G. Bell of New York. Sprague was to be the artist assistant, Bell the taxidermist and preserver. Together they headed for Baltimore where they took the steam car to Cumberland, going from there by stage through the Gap and over the Alleghenies to Wheeling, and from there to Cincinnati on the steamer, *Evelina*. A mail boat relayed them to Louisville.

Through floating ice, intense cold, and equinoctial gales, a squalid steamer, the *Gallant*, carried them and a hundred others on to St. Louis. The settlers on board, bound for the frontier lands, had all their belongings with them—wagons, carts, horses, cows,

and poultry. Audubon and Harris spent their days scanning skies and shores for signs of wild life. Again and again the *Gallant* was grounded, striking a snag at one point with such frightening force that panic resulted—women screamed, babies cried, and dogs barked wildly. Farther on, the *Gallant* began a race with the *Cicero*, which ran her bows against it; and for half a mile the steamers ran perilously locked together. Sixty miles from St. Louis the roof sprang a leak which soaked decks, passengers, and belongings. At length, after picking her way through nearly frozen waters, the *Gallant* docked on March 28. Since 1810, when steamers appeared on the Ohio and in the Mississippi valley, such hazardous runs were typical on the rivers.

Knowing he must wait at least a month for the ice-locked Missouri to open, Audubon resumed his preparations, bought more supplies, conferred with old Pierre Chouteau, famous fur trader who, with his late brother Auguste, had founded the trading post of St. Louis in 1764 on the site of the present city. Chouteau had seen the territory pass from France to Spain and back to France by 1800, witnessed the Louisiana Purchase in 1803 and the formation of Missouri territory in 1812, and finally the formal founding of the city of St. Louis in 1822, twenty-one years before Audubon's visit. An old man of more than ninety years, destined to live a hundred, he was still a good shot and raconteur. Audubon stayed with Nicholas Berthoud, husband of Lucy's sister Eliza, and son of a lady-in-waiting of Marie Antoinette of France and a marquis who had fled the French Revolution. Rather than meet the exorbitant weekly charge of ten dollars for full lodging at the Planter Hotel, the others went to nearby Edwardsville, where they amused themselves with hunting the abundant game.

Already keenly missing home and family, Audubon wrote voluminous letters [8] begging for mail before too late. All communication would soon be suspended. He wished Victor success with the business, and urged both sons, "Finish highly anything you copy from Nature, I pray you." He hoped Lucy would leave off worrying about him, and that his grandchildren would continue to speak his name. Then he turned to the subject of his plans: "I cannot say that I shall finish all my drawings on the spot but I will have them in such condition that they may be perfected at home." The mountaineers and trappers he met in the city markets knew little about game prospects on the Upper Missouri.

On the second of April, Captain Joseph A. Sire, who was to guide the flat-bottomed steamer *Omega* up the Missouri, took him aboard the vessel which was in dry dock for calking. "My stateroom is large," he reported to Victor. "We will have a large table to draw and write on. We will have from eighty to ninety trappers going to the mountains for the Chouteau Concern. They will have the deck floor and live in messes of twelve each, and be fed on corn—unground—boiled in lard or pork . . . There are about thirty boats waiting the breaking up of ice. We have not seen a genteel-looking woman in the streets thus far, and I cannot crow to the beauty of the ladies without *seeing* some of them . . . I wish Johnny to pack up all the skins of quadrupeds and send them to John Bachman, with the injunction that he will not suffer the moths to destroy them. I hope you have placed the original drawings in some room quite handy upstairs, and that you will take precious care of them." He expressed his jubilation at the captain's announcement that there would be several opportunities to put mail ashore as they ascended the Missouri. Countless concerns raced through his mind and found their way into this steady flow of letters: "I do sincerely hope that Victor will be able to meet all his money calls without ever pledging 'Minnie's Land.' To this I never would give my consent under any circumstances. Be industrious, push your collections, rise early in the morning and sit up not late at night, and all will go on well with you." He was receiving "an enormous deal of visits and visitors," ranging from General Gratiot and men of science to trappers and traders. "Many call to see simply what sort of a looking fellow I am," he said. One, a young Mr. Heermann, was the son of an ardent lady admirer and drawing pupil of twenty years before in New Orleans.

Just before the departure Audubon had his long gray locks cut off, and he stored them away with about a hundred skins of birds and quadrupeds and two drawings of squirrels and pocket gophers that he was leaving with Nicholas Berthoud for safekeeping. "You would stare," he wrote, "were you to see me in my Indian hunting shirt." Excitedly he mentioned a gift from his friend Major Mitchell, the manuscript of Lewis and Clark's journal for the year 1805, written in General Clark's hand. This he had to store with other belongings, to lighten what was already far too much baggage for the journey. Though his mind darted about as his excitement rose, it constantly returned to the progress of the *Quadrupeds*. Victor would finish many backgrounds, Audubon hoped. Had Johnny finished a certain drawing of the dogs, he wondered. How many pictures had Victor entered in the current exhibition in New York? He had to report the loss of his last upper tooth, which now obliged him to soak his biscuits. He went on to describe the *Omega's* cargo: "500 dozen eggs, 15 dozens of claret, some brandy and whiskey," food for the trappers—the number of whom had now risen to a hundred and twenty—and for the numerous Indians bound for their wigwams five hundred miles up the Missouri.

Except for Sprague's having temporarily lost his gun in ten feet of water while crossing a bayou on a log, and for Bell's having been severely kicked by a horse, the days in and about St. Louis passed without incident. But Audubon was uneasy to be off. He wrote his sons that the *Omega* was having two strong bulkheads made, one aft and one forward, and that the captain was taking a good keel boat along. "Besides which," he added, "I always rely on that good and kind Providence which has never failed to support me when I was poor, discouraged and in deepest sorrow, when I scarcely knew how I was, or could be, able to support Dearest Mother and you both, my beloved sons . . . Now God bless you all until we all meet again. Give my best remembrances to each and all of our friends and neighbors. I think you have had shad today for din-

[8] National Audubon Society.

ner! I had a fine Wild Turkey hen! Kiss our sweet little ones for me. Kiss your dear wives. Kiss each of yourselves for my sake. Remember me to the servants, the gardener, &c., &c., and believe me for life your husband, friend, father, and that with all possible affection." [9]

Ascent of the Missouri

The *Omega* took her passengers and crew aboard on April 25, 1843, a warm spring day with sunshine. They moved off toward St. Charles at three miles an hour to a deafening salute of farewell from the trappers and their guns on the hurricane deck. Audubon sat in his stateroom, which ordinarily would have been the Ladies Cabin, trying to write a letter [10] in the midst of the din. He said that the trappers—Creoles, half-breeds, and a few Italians—aided and abetted by seven or eight Indians, were keeping up their yelling and singing after the roll call and making it difficult to think. But he was anxious to keep in touch while he could. Speaking of the *Quadrupeds,* he said he hoped to return with about forty drawings including the sketches of antelopes which seemed to be worrying Victor. "When I see you again," he penned in an excited hand on the long crowded page, "I will tell you many a strange fact differing *in toto* from what has been printed in great books." Rather than seek his rest that night with the vermin which infested his cabin, Audubon took his blanket and slept on deck.

His eager scrutiny of sky and shore by day, with glimpses of geese, gray squirrels, white pelicans, teal, cormorants, partridge, and peregrine falcons, filled him with anticipation for sights to come. Every few hours the *Omega* would stop to take on wood cut by the trappers who went ashore for fuel. These stops permitted Audubon and his men to explore the land. "We are quite comfortable for travellers," he reported in one of the rare unpublished Audubon Society letters. "We have passed along ranges of high rocky limestone shores where it would appear birds and beasts retire. Wolves are plentiful, and every farmer drives and confines his sheep each evening for protection. You see how the boat shakes my hand and pen. Therefore I will have, after all, to draw at night instead of during daylight." He turned to the exotic subject of the Indians on board: "The Indian queens have made

us Indian leggings,[11] and mine are ornamented because, said the queen mother, I was an ancient and a medicine man, for I did cure one of the chiefs from sore eyes. When I exhibited my drawings to the whole group they knew about all of the animals and laughed curiously, and said that if I would go to their villages I would be treated as a Great Man! It was much the same at St. Louis when I also showed them to some Indians of other tribes."

When the *Omega* reached the mouth of the Missouri, Audubon again produced his *Quadrupeds* plates to show the Indians on shore: "The effect was beyond belief . . . One of the women actually ran off at the sight of the woodchucks, exclaiming that they were alive. The chiefs knew all the animals except the little squirrels from the Oregon. Their signs were most significant, and the interpreter told us of their delight . . . They called me the Great Divine." They told him some tall stories about the animals in his plates. This brought him to thoughts of how the work in New York might be progressing, and he reminded Victor of his artistic role in addition to subscriptions: "I hope that Victor will have begun painting backgrounds. Now the blossoms and young leaves of the oaks are perfectly beautiful and would look well with any species of squirrels."

Just which backgrounds in the various plates were done by Victor is, in the last analysis, a matter for conjecture. Probably all true landscapes, especially those containing houses and human figures, as well as those with animal figures by John Woodhouse Audubon in which striking floral detail is included, are Victor's. Definite attribution is not possible. Of the first fifty plates, it is reasonable to surmise that J. J. Audubon executed many of these in their entirety, as for example the two original studies for Say's Chipmunk, page 165, done in August 1834, and signed and dated by him. However, few of the existing signed and dated water color originals contain more than the figures of the mammals. The water color for the print of the Large Striped Skunk, page 112, by Audubon bears this interesting, possibly unique, penciled direction—whether to himself for later on, or for Victor, must remain uncertain: "To be placed on the rock, and the young beneath it, so as to render them almost imperceptible in the shadows." Like others in the Pierpont Morgan Library Collection, the margin is enriched by penciled details of hind and fore feet, "size of

---

[9] National Audubon Society.   [10] National Audubon Society.   [11] American Museum of Natural History.

nature," drawn, like the figures, at Minnie's Land in 1843. Probably many or most of the backgrounds for his son John's figures were by Victor. John followed the paternal method of arranging the animal subject in a lifelike attitude, both in oils and water color, but oftenest in the former, unlike Audubon senior.

As the artist passed through the Black Snake Hills his thoughts returned to the Hudson: "The country about you must be beautiful, and I hope that dear Victor will lose no opportunity in finishing backgrounds. We have seen nothing yet worthy of our pencils, as the prairies are not out in blossom." Just beyond the nation of the Kickapoos and opposite the lands of the Sacs, the "aspect of the wonderful river" began changing. The waters narrowed and sent a strong current around the huge sand bars that had delayed the *Omega* for hours a few days earlier. Audubon looked forward to nightly trapping beyond Council Bluffs. He had been contenting himself with shooting game during the overnight and woodcutting stops.

Audubon described the two-day delay in Council Bluffs, then in the Iowa territory, opposite Omaha and the Nebraska lands, Iowa not having been admitted to the Union until 1846 or three years after the artist's visit. The federal inspectors examined the cargo for smuggled spirits which might lead to Indian uprisings if used in trade. Captain Sire's well-hidden supply went undetected, but it is doubtful whether its safety concerned Audubon, a temperate man who often boasted that he had never so much as tasted wine until after his marriage. A few of the Indians aboard disembarked, and the Sac chief rode off across the prairie on his pony. Indians had come running to meet their returning tribesmen, some on foot, others astride horses, riding bareback or in Spanish saddles. "Even the squaws rode, and rode well, too!" However, no greetings were exchanged, and the greeters seemed interested only in the food supplies brought from St. Louis.

The Iowa and Fox Indians' sugar camps with their well-made canoe-shaped bark troughs impressed Audubon favorably, but his disappointment in the Red Man was increasing. Again and again he derided the painter George Catlin's idealized accounts of them in his writings and through his pictures, without heed for their vicissitudes

since Catlin's travels. "The rascals stole a good knife from us," his letter [12] of May 8 complained. "They are cunning beyond conception. We will have to be on the alert when any of them call on a visit."

It is almost incredible that such was the scene a mere hundred and eight years ago in country that the same letter referred to as "positively out of the United States boundaries westward." The territory in which Audubon said, "All the people we will see will be Indians, Indians and nothing but Indians," is now hundreds of miles of the country's richest wheat and corn lands, with thriving cities and nowhere an Indian to be seen. Furthermore, the Audubon party even had to carry permits issued by the government for entry into this untamed territory.

Audubon had about a hundred quadruped and bird specimens from the daily hunting forays on shore. He began to sound accustomed to the wilderness: [13] "We are all *perfectly well* and fattening fast. My beard begins to curl, and my cropped hair has altered my looks somewhat, but my heart is still the same and I hope to return to you with much knowledge and *bonne santé* next autumn. We have not struck a single snag, though we have rubbed some fallen trees pretty hard. We stuck on a sand bar for a night and part of two days."

He went on to describe the damage of spring floods in this Bluffs country eight hundred miles above St. Louis: "The entire channel of this tremendous stream has been all more or less changed, and this renders the navigation quite intricate. The bottom lands have been completely inundated and the general devastation is beyond conception or description. Many, many cabins have been abandoned—fences, fields—all are gone to some new land elsewhere. The people are in a state of starvation never known before; not a sign of cultivation have we seen since we passed the Black Snake Hills, not a plough . . . and it is doubtful whether any crop will be raised by white or red man this season. Glorious time, this, for the geese, ducks and gulls which are treading all over these great plains, now of mud and water instead of the lovely flowers of this season . . . The hills are nearly bare of timber and have no underwood or brushwood . . . No one going down to New Orleans some twenty years ago can have an idea of the snags and dangers of this 'Upper Missouri,' which are like thousands of mam-

---

[12] National Audubon Society.

[13] National Audubon Society.

MARMOTTE DE SAVOYE (GROUND HOG) (*above*). This is the earliest known mammal drawing by J. J. Audubon. It was made during a visit to France, when he was twenty years old. Crayon on paper. 20¼" x 26½". Dated June 6, 1805. (Harvard University Library)

AUDUBON FINDS HIS BIRD DRAWINGS DESTROYED BY NORWAY RATS (*right*). Japanese print from Nakamura Mesano's *The Western Countries' Book of Successful Careers*, a Japanese translation of Samuel Smiles's book, *Self Help*, published in 1859. (Bella C. Landauer Collection in The New York Historical Society)

J.J.A.

AMERICAN HARES (*above and left*). Original studies for Fig. 60, page 131. The background as worked separately and later incorporated into the finished lithograph. (The American Museum of Natural History)

SPANIEL SURPRISING ENGLISH PHEASANTS (*below*). This version, one of three, was painted in Edinburgh in 1827, and hung for years in the Audubon parlor at Minnie's Land. It is now in the collection of The American Museum of Natural History. Oil. 57″ x 93″. N.B. The second version, said to have been painted for presentation to King George IV, who died before its completion, now hangs in the Racquet and Tennis Club, New York. The third version, in water color, is privately owned.

J.J.A.

J.W.A.

DEER (*above*). Water color. 37″ x 28″. Dated March 16, 1844. (The American Museum of Natural History)

HEAD OF A DEER (*left*). Water color. 12″ x 10″. (The American Museum of Natural History)

J.W.A.

DEER

Oil. 38" x 60".

(The Brooklyn Museum) *J.J.A. or J.W.A.*

HEAD OF A DOE (*opposite page*). Water color made during Audubon's Missouri river expedition (see page 45). A legend on the back of the original reads: "Head of doe shot at Fort Union by Edward Harris and drawn by me. John J. Audubon. June 30 and July 1, 1843." Water color drawing, life size. (Collection of Mrs. Richard Graham; photograph courtesy of Stanley Clisby Arthur)

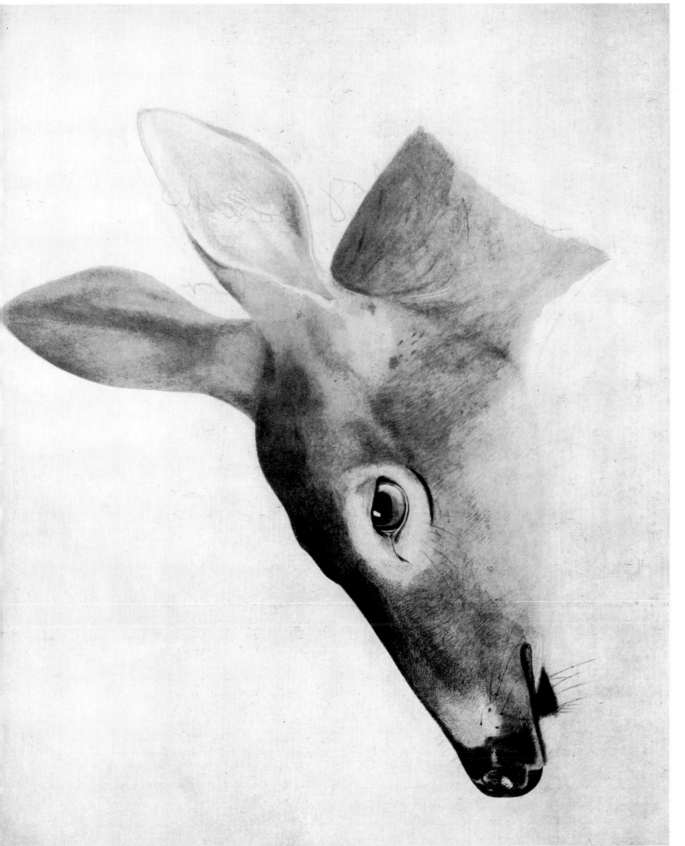

J.J.A.

(Description on opposite page.)

HEAD OF A DOE

SHEEP (*above left*). Probably by J. W. Audubon. Pencil drawing and opaque white on paper. 10″ x 14″. DOGS (*above right*). Attributed to J. W. Audubon. Pencil drawing. 10″ x 14″. Both purchased from J. J. Audubon's widow, Lucy Audubon. (The New York Historical Society) BULL (*center*). Attributed to J. J. Audubon. Acquired from Leonard Audubon, a descendant, and presented to the National Gallery of Art of the United States by E. J. L. Hallstrom of Sydney, Australia. Oil. 20″ x 14″. HORSES (*left*). Attributed to J. W. Audubon. Purchased from Lucy Audubon. Pencil drawing with white on paper. 10″ x 14″. (The New York Historical Society)

EAGLE AND LAMB (*right*). Painted in England in 1827, the original hung for many years in the bedroom of Lucy Audubon at Minnie's Land. Oil. 58″ x 93″. (National Audubon Society; photograph: The Old Print Shop, Inc.) FOX AND GOOSE (*center*). Oil. 21½″ x 33¾″. (Butler Art Institute, Youngstown, Ohio) OTTER AND TROUT (*below*). Oil. 12″ x 18″. (Ferargil Gallery, New York)

J.J.A.

J.J.A.

J.J.A.

HEAD OF A BUFFALO CALF

A legend on the back of the original in Audubon's hand reads "Head of Buffalo Calf two months old, procured near Fort George."
The study was made during the journey to the Missouri headwaters in 1843. Water color and ink. 26″ x 32¼″. (Collection of
Frank H. Shaffer, Jr., Cincinnati, Ohio)

moth elk horns planted to impede navigation . . . The vegetation in the high prairies has scarcely begun, and this will greatly retard the expedition of those bound for Santa Fe, whose waggons and carts await their arrival at Independence, the usual point of departure."

This previously unpublished letter (which was to be relayed from Council Bluffs in the monthly ride to Fort Leavenworth, Kansas, and on to New York) ended on a homesick note: "All around you must now look beautiful . . . the trees in full leaf. Perhaps in ten days from this place the grass on the upper prairies will suffice to feed the mules and some of the travellers. How beautiful our garden must be just now. How dearly our sweet children must enjoy the green grass, and all the blossoms and butterflies that wing their way through our manor. What fine fish you must be catching. Oh how dearly I should like to be with you tomorrow all day, and back again here the next. I do most sincerely hope that Victor will be able to manage our money calls until my return, and that he will finish many backgrounds as well as procure subscribers to both the *Quadrupeds* and the little edition of the *Birds*, for now I cannot help him for some time to come. I should like to see dear Johnny's chickens, and ducks, and turkey pullets as they grow up, as well as his potatoes, turnips, &c. Cut few and plant many is my motto. Take care of each and all of you . . . my blessings, my dearest friends . . . Kiss the darlings for me, and dearest mother. I hope all our English friends are well, and when you write, remember me there also, and now goodnight to all of you, for you have gone to rest, I hope, and about 1½ hours ago. Rise early and work hard, and again God bless you all. Forever your affectionate friend, husband and father, J. J. Audubon." Errant nineteenth century sentimentality this, perhaps; however, not to hear Audubon speak such language, as he did during his whole lifetime, is not to know the man he was.

May was a time of changing scenery, sunshine, spring freshets, birds and bird migrations, countless quadrupeds—deer, antelope, wild cat, elk, and wolf. Taking it for a new species, Audubon named a Western Fox Squirrel, shot by Bell, for his son John. He had Sprague make an outline which he himself planned to develop in water color. One day their serenity was interrupted by some shots at the fleeing *Omega*. A band of Indians, signaling to the captain

to stop and let them stare at the steamer and all who were aboard, were furious at his refusal and turned their guns on them. Despite this, the steamer escaped undamaged.

The middle of May produced signs of what they might expect to find a hundred miles onward. A dead buffalo cow and calf, two of thousands that died in the heavy snows or drowned in the river, floated down stream. At military posts farther on, the party was advised to proceed with caution on their rambles ashore because of hostile feeling between Indian and trapper due to general distrust, misunderstanding, and occasional murdering. Audubon seemed disturbed by the presence of so many half-breed children in these settlements where officials took Indian wives. Not even the assurance that they would receive a proper education in St. Louis quite removed his skepticism. Never did he seem to take into account the reasons for the swift deterioration of these people, whom he called "dirty, rascally and verminous rascals."

An unpublished letter of May 24 tells how he saw a scow-shaped boat approaching, made of a light wooden frame covered with buffalo hide. In it were a French Creole trapper and a companion bound for Fort Vermilion, who shouted that they had made the 125-mile voyage from Fort Pierre in nine days time. Next day a group of three Mackinaw barges, their roofs laden with buffalo meat, drew up alongside the *Omega* for the trappers on all four vessels to exchange their news.

The stream was beginning to be filled with the carcasses of buffaloes destroyed by the snows. Live ones swam across the steamer's path without heed of danger. Audubon estimated that between daylight and noon on May 28, they had sighted more than two thousand buffaloes on the prairies, not far from Fort George on the left bank of the river in what is now Lyman County, South Dakota. At Fort George he was overjoyed when a young Englishman named Illingsworth who was in charge of the establishment brought him his first buffalo to sketch at the fort, a two-month-old buffalo calf, and the head of another—quite possibly the one illustrated opposite. After Sprague took an outline the size of nature, Bell put the whole calf in brine. A day or two later Audubon mentioned: "Sprague and I have drawn the head. Sprague will make final outlines of very young calves with the *camera lucida* and group them to form part of the plate of the buffalo."

After many difficulties, the *Omega* reached Fort Pierre, three miles above the mouth of the Teton river on the last day of May. In another absorbing letter in the National Audubon Society Collection dated June 1, Audubon wrote this description:

My Dearest Friends: . . .We have been detained here, one plate of the boilers having been burnt out. We have hunted far and wide—Deer, Elk, Wolves, but have seen nothing. One of our deck hands killed a *very large* doe that had three fawns in her, and carried her nearly three miles on his back, Indian fashion. The country, destitute of trees, looks desolate in the extreme . . . We have two species of new birds, perhaps three . . . a good number of skins both of quadrupeds and birds, and in two or three days we will be amongst herds of buffaloes, antelopes, black-tailed deer . . .

Our good captain gave me a fine buck elk which he has alive at Fort Pierre, and also a superb pair of antlers. We will show you, I trust, some fine drawings when we get home. Johnny would have enjoyed this trip well, for he would have seen many new things . . . the many water birds . . . the gophers exceedingly abundant, now at work in the bottomlands. Harris thinks the rats must have got up the trees to save themselves during that awful visitation. I find that walking fatigues me with boots on . . . I will go in moccasins. Yesterday two rattlesnakes were brought in, of a species new to us all. Wolves are abundant . . . and yellow-headed troupials, ravens, ground larks, finches. I have seen only a few trees new to me, and not a flower. These prairies are by no means as prolific as those of Illinois and Indiana, all Mr. Catlin says to the contrary. I keep my journals full of all I see, do and hear when our captain says I may rely on the reports . . . We saw black-tailed deer several days ago, running on the shore, and also a fine black Bear swimming across the river. Many rifles were shot at Bruin but he kept on his course to the shore, and found great difficulty in getting up the bank, fell backward several times, but at last got up and started at a gallop . . .

I trust that Victor will be able to manage the cash business, and have a famous set of backgrounds most highly finished when I return. I hope also that Bowen [the printer] will not disgrace us or himself by giving us indifferent work, and lastly I hope you may procure a good number of subscribers. If it is true that Daniel Webster has resigned his office will he pay the drafts he promised to accept and to pay?[14] We have seen little scenery that would have proved attractive to Victor, but for a few fine sunsets and some groups of Indians . . . Neither Harris, Squires nor myself have shaved since we left St. Louis, and I have not once pulled off my breeches when I have tumbled down at night to go to sleep . . .

I hope you have sent a copy of No. 2 of the *Quadrupeds* to John Bachman—nay I suppose that you have No. 3 nearly ready for delivery [ten plates in each number]. I wish you to send me to St. Louis all the plates that you get, so that I may receive them after September 15th; I think I may procure a few subscribers . . .

I hope that Victor sends some extracts of each of my letters to the newspaper editors. It cannot do any harm and may chance to do some good. The men belonging to the Santa Fe expedition who were taken prisoner and carried to the city of Mexico [tell] tales curious and wonderful if true, but I have not dared to write them in my Journal. I prefer keeping as much as possible [of the Journal's contents] for our books on quadrupeds. But you may find some extracts of interest for publication . . .

Squires has been making a map of the river, since Council Bluffs; it may assist us on the return. Bell skins everything worth having. Sprague makes a few sketches. I write in my Journal and Harris takes notes on geology. Last night we sent eight hunters out. They killed four buffaloes. Tougher flesh I never tried to grind down. In two days it may become tender. The hunters saw thirty Antelopes and some very large white wolves. The country is covered with Buffaloes . . .

Write to John Bachman to prepare as much of the letter-press as he possibly can in manuscript, to which we may add all that I collect of good information . . .

Postscript. Bell, Squires and I walked to the Fort Pierre and found Mr. Picotte, who was so kind as to present me with several articles of Indian wearing apparel, a necklace of the Grizzly Bear's claws, and the largest, finest and best-prepared elk skin[15] ever procured in this country . . . I have an Indian whip that will astonish Johnny, and I am sending you an Indian lodge of great dimensions that I wish you to place, until the approach of winter, in the sweet spot that overlooks the river, and to take in before frost. If well put up with 19 or 21 poles, Indian fashion, Victor and our good friend James Hall will dearly enjoy their smoking from beneath it. Unfortunately there are no handsome moccasins at this fort, or I would have quite a mess . . . wait a while and I will supply you . . .

---

[14] Webster's subscription was proving a decided worry.

[15] American Museum of Natural History Collection.

The ascent of the river was endlessly panoramic. The sight of an old Riccaree Indian village one day would be followed on the next by an active or abandoned military post; or a passing barge-load of trappers resembling nothing so much as "Pyrenees bandits"; or the site of a steamer's burning, already a tragic legend.

On June 7 Fort Clark, some twelve hundred miles above the mouth of the Missouri, came in view on the right bank, with its clusters of perhaps a hundred mud huts of the Mandan Village all around it, and its small corn, bean and pumpkin fields under cultivation. Earlier this was the scene of a great battle for supremacy betwen the Riccaree and Mandan tribes. Everything was put under lock and key against pilfering by the "poor miserable devils" in robes and blankets already gathering on the banks. Answering the Fort's salute, the *Omega* steamed for shore. Audubon and Harris took a walk up the bluff to the fort. The artist was immediately given a buffalo headdress and a live Swift Fox which was chained in a loft. They explored the squalid Mandan Village, first entering the lodge of the Medicine Man, then one of the dark, muddy huts filled with squaws and children. From a cauldron that hung from the roof they were served a mixture of pemmican and corn in buffalo horn spoons. These people were the survivors of a small-pox epidemic a decade before so devastating that it had destroyed more Riccarees and Mandans than had all their battles.

The American Indian's sorry state again depressed Audubon. He was hardly amused that same evening by a visitation from the Gros Ventres "braves" who came aboard in buffalo robes, cock's plume headdresses, bright moccasins, and leggings, to which shoulder epaulets lent a touch of pale-face grandeur. With sad contempt he saw them take gifts of coffee, biscuits, and tobacco—these aborigines who had asked the *Omega's* captain on a previous trip whether he fed the boat whisky to spur it on when it was weary. Audubon was glad to see the last of Fort Clark, which to him was a small inferior copy of Fort Pierre.

By now the party had decided on good advice to abandon the idea of entering the treacherous Rockies, land of the Blackfeet Indians. They would go only as far as Fort Union, at the mouth of the Yellowstone, no great distance from the Canadian border, and remain until mid-August, when Audubon hoped to hunt in the Bad Lands of the Dakotas. They were in increasingly remote frontier country, with buffalo hunting an almost daily occurrence, but, afoot, less thrilling than they were to find it on horseback later. Audubon often rose at three for a few hours of hunting needed specimens—elk, geese, grouse, and small birds—before the *Omega*, which was tied up overnight, steamed ahead. Then he would try to draw despite the boat's "horrible motion."

Four days beyond Fort Clark the journey was interrupted by a sudden blaze in the boat's stern which was set by hot cinders. As there were ten thousand pounds of gun powder below in the hold, the apprehension of all aboard can be imagined. Fortunately the flames were quickly extinguished and Audubon again had reason to be grateful that disaster had been averted, and that Providence had once more given him protection.

At Fort Union

On June 12, 1843, the *Omega* neared Fort Union. It had made the voyage of some 1400 miles in forty-eight days and seven hours, a record run for a distance covered today by train in a day or two at the longest! The bearded Audubon stood at the rail, tense with anticipation as they steamed past Fort Opposition, three miles below their final destination. The fort ran up flags in greeting. Never had Audubon ceased to entertain the dread that perhaps their ascent of the Missouri would not be accomplished, for it was well known that river travel was full of hazards, such as he had experienced. But now at last, they were arriving!

At five on that showery, windy evening the *Omega* sighted Fort Union in the distance on the east bank and at seven they heard her thunderous welcoming salute, answered by six guns from the steamer as it put to shore. As the sounds reverberated up and down the river, a cavalcade cantered down the banks, and in a few minutes all was bustle and confusion. Captain Sire, Audubon, and his party went ashore. Alexander Culbertson, a young Englishman who was the fort's chief agent and who had headed the welcoming party of riders, stepped forward to extend official greetings. After all had been introduced, Audubon and his men walked to the fort, were given a swift and bumpy ride around the prairie in an old wagon which whisked them over the flat, scraggly wastes for a view of the distant hills and the beclouded sunset. They returned to the *Omega* for dinner with Captain Sire and at his invitation remained aboard for the night. Their state of excitement was complete as they pitched in to help with the unloading of cargo, and with the reloading for Sire's return down the Missouri. And they made haste to write letters for him to carry as far as St. Louis for the mails, their last chance until autumn to send word home.

By six on the night of June 13, Audubon wrote that his head was so full he could scarcely order his impressions; and his pen and hand trembled so with excitement that he had to give up, and hope for another chance to send a message down the river. But he managed to say that he was sending a box of bird and quadruped specimens, and some bundles of skins, and a pair of elk horns with the *Omega* to Chouteau in St. Louis, as well as a copy of his journal up to that day. He mentioned the thrilling sight of twenty-two mountain rams and ewes in a flock on the hills at the mouth of the Yellowstone river; and he spoke of the abundance of wolves and grizzlies. He closed with the usual affection—for Lucy, his grandchildren, all—and with the hope that his sons were busy with the publications and the fields and gardens, while promising that he and Sprague would be busy hunting and drawing specimens.

Captain Sire made ready to put the *Omega* about and return to St. Louis. Audubon, grateful for the party's safe conduct, gave him a fine "six-barrelled pistol" with the wish that he might never have to use it in self-defense, and handed him this somehow touchingly grandiose word of thanks:

Dear Sir,—We cannot part with you previous to your return to St. Louis, without offering to you our best wishes, and our thanks for your great courtesy, assuring you how highly we appreciate, and feel grateful for your uniform kindness and gentlemanly deportment to each and all of us. We are most happy to add that our passage . . . has been devoid of any material accident, which we can only attribute to the great regularity and constant care with which you have discharged your arduous duties in the difficult navigation of the river.

We regret that it is not in our power . . . to offer you a suitable token of our esteem, but hope you will confer on us the favor of accepting at our hands a six-barrelled, silver-mounted pistol, which we sincerely hope and trust you may never have occasion to use in defence of your person. We beg you to consider us,

Your well-wishers and friends—.

As the *Omega* set out, and as her guns and the fort's cannon exchanged salutes, the squaws and children on the prairies "howled, fell down on the earth, or ran in every direction," and the dogs bolted off in terror.

Begun by a Scot named McKenzie in 1829, Fort Union, six and a half miles above the mouth of the Yellowstone, was the handsomest trading post on the river. Situated close to the Missouri's banks, it was flanked by an expanse of prairie land ascending to bluffs footed by thickly wooded bottom lands. At two corners of the twenty-foot-high cottonwood stockade were huge whitewashed stone bastions. Balconies circled the two upper stories, with observatories from which watch was kept of the prairies. Two sixty-foot flagpoles flew the Stars and Stripes and the American Eagle, and two weathervanes—a buffalo and an eagle—were silhouetted against the immense skies. Behind the bastions' portholes were cannon, a loaded brass swivel, and a stack of muskets, always ready in case of Indian attack.

The fort's main building was papered within and decked with pictures. It contained an office, living apartments, a mess hall, saddlery room, and tailor's shop. Another building contained storerooms, a retail shop, warehouse, and a press room to hold as many as three thousand buffalo robes and other furs and peltries. A third building housed the clerks, and another the hunters. Adjoining the mess hall was a kitchen, behind which stood an icehouse, hen house, milk house and dairy, and a cooper's shop. The structures included stables for the horses and cattle, with blacksmith, gunsmith, and tinner shops besides. On top of the huge front gates was painted a treaty scene between Indians and settlers. An extra pair of gates just inside the portals led to a reception room and trade shop for visiting Indians, which had no entry or access to the fort proper. To the east was a large enclosure for storing hay; and half a mile off lay an acre and a half of vegetable gardens.

Audubon and his men were finally assigned to a large chamber occupied ten years earlier by Maximilian, Prince of Wied, during his expedition for American fauna. Squires arranged his buffalo robe on the couch of the foreign prince. Their first night of rest was interrupted by the lively strains of clarinets, fiddles, and drums below, the arrival of the trappers having called for a celebration. "There was no alternative," Audubon's journal tells. "We all got up and in a short time were amid the *beau monde* of these parts. Several squaws, attired in their best, were present, trappers, clerks, &c. Mr. Culbertson played the fiddle very fairly, Mr. Guèpe played the clarinet, and Mr. Chouteau the drum as if brought up in the art of the Great Napoleon. Cotillions and reels were danced until one o'clock."

Audubon eagerly showed his *Quadrupeds* plates, and many persons volunteered their help in finding specimens. He sent a trapper off for antelope, a practice he was commonly to follow, while he, Harris and the others went hunting. A bargeman gave him a pet badger and Culbertson a fine gray wolf which Audubon began drawing. A young deer fawn was brought in for the same purpose. Buffaloes were a common sight from the balconies, and the cows and calves nearby were gentle enough to approach if one did not touch them. Audubon was grieved when a Kit Fox, which was kept tied to the foot of a ladder, met its death when bundles of buffalo robes fell on it from a loft above.

Culbertson lost no time in proposing a sham buffalo hunt for the benefit of the newcomers. A new suit of clothes was to be the prize to the one who could fire the most shots and reload while running full speed. "We were all delighted to see these feats," Audubon wrote in his journal. "The horses ran at a full gallop." He praised Culbertson's astonishing horsemanship, and said the Englishman would not have taken four hundred dollars for his Blackfoot pony, adding, "I should like to see some of the best English gentlemen hunt in like manner." The agent promised them a real buffalo hunt soon.

One hunting excursion succeeded another under the leadership of Audubon's Indian guide, Alexis. The game was brought back to the fort by mule cart and ferry from the wilds across the river, for Bell to dismember or skin and clean, or put in boiled brine for safekeeping and future study. One prize was a fine old male antelope, the head of which Audubon began outlining at once. The first outline was a small drawing made with the *camera lucida,* the second a large one on squared-off paper. Sprague worked alongside him at the same subject. It is ironical that so few of the Upper Missouri sketches and drawings have survived, many having been lost in a fire of the 1870's.

A day in late June found Audubon at his drawing board at 5 A.M., at work on the head of a doe. This water color is illustrated on page 37. He would work in the early hours of the morning almost ceaselessly until about three in the afternoon. On June 30, he wrote, "Becoming fatigued for want of practice, I took a short walk, regretting I could no longer draw twelve or fourteen hours without a pause or thought of weariness."

All about him, as he labored, pulsed the life of Fort Union. He was interrupted, now by a visitor with a Red-shafted Flicker brought down by a bow and arrow, now by the hammers of carpenters at work on a new ferryboat to replace the Union's stolen skiff; or, as he sketched, he listened to the latest rumors of the Sioux and Gros Ventres uprisings, battles, and murders.

With only a few fireworks sent up from the ramparts, the Fourth of July of that year was the quietest in Audubon's memory. All day long he had devoted himself to drawing the head of a Bighorn. Beside him sat Sprague, beginning a portrait of Culbertson who, while he fidgeted in his chair, talked of buffaloes, and how, during the winter just past, they were so abundant that at night they came close to the fort and picked up wisps of straw dropped by the hay carts. He said that he had strewn hay to lure them into the old fort used as a hog and cattle shelter beside Fort Union, but that they would come no farther than the gates. Large herds slept near the main entrance, but by dawn would move off to the hills, returning again toward nightfall.

Audubon had finished a successful likeness of Mrs. Culbertson, whom he found a pleasing subject despite the hard-riding, comely Blackfoot princess' restlessness. She had much curiosity about his art, and seemed to Audubon superior to most of her race. He found her handsome and refined in most ways, though he deplored her fondness for warm raw buffalo brains, which she ate with all too evident relish. One day she swam gracefully out into the Missouri after six Mallard ducklings which she caught by hand, thinking Audubon might like to sketch them. Like all her tribe she took decided pride in her expert swimming. She and Culbertson presented the artist with many trophies to carry home as reminders of their friendship. A number of these are to be seen, along with other mementoes, in the American Museum of Natural History in New York: a Blackfoot saddle and stirrups, leather breeches, a fine knife case, full Indian regalia, and a parfleche, or decorated hide of superb workmanship.

Then Audubon, after watching Sprague, decided to try his own luck with a portrait of the Englishman. Like his princess he found it hard to sit quietly, and when he had had enough he would rise, and Audubon would turn to the wolf's head at which he was also working. Or he and the Culbertsons would ride forth on the prairies. Or he would take up his gun and join Harris and Bell for a hunt along the river. Such outings invariably yielded new sketches for his portfolios—mammals, sugar loaf cactus, buffalo berries—or they increased his collection of seeds.

Sprague, meanwhile, abandoned his portrait of Culbertson to cross the river and begin a view of Fort Union from the opposite shore. One afternoon while he was thus engaged, and while Audubon was painting the agent, the word was passed that a party of fourteen Assiniboin Indians had been sighted with the telescope. The approaching braves in all their war paint and clumsy buffalo robes began yelling and singing to the steps of their scalp dance, to inform their observers up in the ramparts that they had killed their enemy in battle. As victors they were a forlorn-looking lot, with only three guns, some lances, and their knives among them. The leader, however, brandished a club studded with butcher knives. A few Indian women went outside the gates of the fort to meet them, and the warriors painted the face of one squaw black as a sign of friendship. They had come to trade buffalo flesh for dried meat and tobacco. Two days of almost continuous singing to their monotonous scalp dance ended in Culbertson's taking away their drum and insisting that they leave. There is an account of the recent battle of these Indians in Audubon's journal:

"Their party at first consisted of nearly fifty. They travelled several hundred miles in search of Blackfeet, and discovering a small troop of them they hid till the next morning. (Daylight is always the time they prefer for an attack.) They rushed upon the enemy, surprised them, killed one, and the rest took flight, leaving guns, horses, shields, lances on the ground. The Assiniboins took several guns and seven horses, and the scalp of the dead Indian. The man they killed had, some time before, killed the father of their chief. They followed the trail of the Blackfeet, but not seeing them they separated into small parties, and it is one of these parties that is now with us. The chief, to show his pride and delight at killing his enemy, has borrowed a drum, and they have nearly ever since been yelling, singing, and beating that beastly tambour."

On July 11 a buck brought in by the hunters seemed to Audubon so exceptionally beautiful that he could scarcely wait for dawn to begin the drawing. He was up at three and had Bell arranging the animal as he wished it. He worked steadily until noonday dinner, leaving his table only long enough to watch a wolf give chase to a horse and rider. In the afternoon he returned to the Culbertson portrait, and after finishing it he framed and hung it, to the delight of the sitter and the princess. However, he himself felt that it might have been better.

The arrival of midsummer brought many adventures in buffalo hunting. Audubon's and Harris' journals carry long accounts of its pursuit; Lewis Squires, expedition secretary, who proved the most venturesome member of the party, also wrote a description. So absorbed did they all become with it for about a fortnight, that it is no wonder that John Bachman, watchfully waiting in Charleston for Audubon's new memoranda, was to write him caustically about his neglect of the small rodents for the fascination of the bison.

Audubon put aside his earlier misgivings as to the wisdom of joining the hunts on horseback, though he wisely kept clear of the central skirmishes, following and keenly watching the younger riders and observing the lines of the animals and their characteristic movements. Feats of horsemanship were Fort Union's main diversion, whether at sham buffalo hunts or real wolf-chasing just outside the gates. At such a wild race as one held on the nearby prairie on July 14, Audubon was only a willing onlooker.

First Squires had donned Audubon's Indian dress, and Mrs. Culbertson had painted his face and that of another visitor to resemble demons. Then she and her Indian maidservant, her husband, Squires, and three other horsemen all dashed "like wild creatures of unearthly compound" across a ravine after a wolf. They whipped their horses and rode for it, and after an arrow missed, a bullet stopped its flight. Squires accounted for himself so superbly in the saddle that the princess, herself a strong and wonderful rider, said he was the equal of any horseman in the territory.

Early next morning they all set out on a two-day excursion along the Yellowstone, with a wagon pulling a skiff on a cart for crossings. Audubon narrowly escaped with his life soon after they sighted buffaloes. He and his horse advanced on an enraged bull, but instead of veering to one side he rode directly past it. Looking back he saw the bull only three feet behind him, ready to gore him had he not managed to turn and gallop off while Bell dropped the animal with a shot through the shoulder.

A few days later they encountered more buffaloes, and the ensuing hunt Audubon describes in his journal. The passage will scarcely warm the heart of the conservationist of our own less ruthless day. It is quoted not because it is an experience for any modern hunter to envy, but as a frank picture of a frontier activity engaged in at the time with little or no sense of guilt in the face of an incredible abundance. It will be seen, however, that after a few such days of hunting, Audubon feared for the buffalo's chances of survival against such odds, and much of the spectacle made him sick at heart. The passage which follows has never before been reprinted:

July 20th. We were up early, and had our breakfast shortly after four, and before eight had left the landing. We had two carts this time. Mr. C. drove Harris, Bell and myself. The others rode on the carts and led the hunting horses, or runners as they are called. As we neared the Fox River someone espied four Buffaloes. Our heads were soon turned towards them. We travelled to within half a mile of them, concealed by a ridge or hill. The wind was favorable and we moved on slowly. Owen and Mr. Culbertson had their heads bound with handkerchiefs. I crawled on the ridge with the others and saw the bulls running away, but in a direction favorable for us to see the chase.

On the word of command the horses were let loose and away went the hunters. Two bulls ran together and Mr. C. and Bell followed, then one after another of the hunters. Mr. C. shot first, and his bull stopped at the fire, walked towards where I was, and halted about sixty yards from me. . . .

Bell and Mr. C. went after the second bull, Harris took the third, and Squires the fourth. Bell's shot took effect in the buttock, and Mr. Culbertson shot, placing his ball a few inches above or below Bell's. At this moment Squires' horse threw him over his head, fully ten feet. He fell on his powder-horn and was severely bruised. He cried to Harris to catch his horse, and he was on his legs at once, but felt sick for a few minutes. Harris, cool as a cucumber, neared his bull, shot it through the lungs, and it fell dead on the spot. Bell was now in full pursuit of his game. Harris joined Squires and followed the fourth, which, however, was soon out of my sight. But the weather was hot, and being afraid of injuring their horses they let the fourth bull make his escape.

Bell's bull fell on his knees, got up again, and rushed on him. The animal, shot again, stood a minute with his tail partially elevated, and then fell dead. Having no knife with him, Bell did not bring the tongue with him as is customary. The first bull —which Mr. Culbertson insisted on calling my bull —was fat and soon skinned and cut up. Harris was seated on his bull, to which we walked, and the same ceremony took place. Mr. C. broke open the head of "my" bull and ate part of the brains raw, and so did many of the others, even Squires. The very sight of this turned my stomach.

Squires, the most daring of Audubon's party, nearly met his end on July 26, when a group of nine started after buffalo cows. Seeing a bull late one evening near the Blackfoot river, at a moment when meat was needed for supper in camp, they agreed to let Squires try and get it. The bull, wounded, furiously began charging Squires, Culbertson, and Owen. According to Audubon's account, Squires then "ran between the bull and a ravine quite close to the animal. It suddenly turned on him. His horse, frightened, jumped into the ravine, and the bull followed. Squires now lost his balance, threw his gun down, clung to the mane of his horse and recovered his seat. The horse got away and saved his life. The bull would have killed him in a few minutes, as Mr. C. and Owen had only empty guns. Squires told us

he had never been so bewildered and terrified before."

Audubon's journal for August 5 reveals his view
of the buffalo's chances of survival, as well as his
ultimate feelings about the sport. He was writing as
a man of fifty-eight who because of his years, and
the fact that his main interest was in accurately de-
picting the animals, had been mostly an observer on
the hunts. One of the old hands around the fort told
him that the animals died not by the score but by
the hundreds during the deep snows of winter. The
description of their plight deeply perturbed him. So
did the realization of "the immense numbers that
are murdered almost daily on these boundless
wastes called prairies—the hosts that are drowned
in the freshets, and the hundreds of calves who die
in early spring." He could hardly conceive how so
many were still to be seen, the sight of them becoming as commonplace as cattle at home in eastern
pastures. "But this cannot last," he sadly reflected,
"even now there is a perceptible difference in the
size of the herds, and before many years the Buffalo,
like the Great Auk, will have disappeared; surely
this should not be permitted." Such sentiments suggest that he would side today with the hundreds of
Audubon Societies which strive for the conservation of our disappearing wild life, and be proud that
such a movement bears his name.

By early August a forty-foot Mackinaw boat was
being built at Fort Union for the party's return voyage to St. Louis; it was already, Audubon said, "looking pretty." The *Union* was to be its name, in honor
of the united spirit which had made the expedition
a success. Audubon had eleven new bird species to
take home, and his notebooks were crammed with
sketches, data, and descriptions for the *Quadrupeds*, but he was continuing his efforts to draw all
the best specimens available: "I have been drawing
the head of one of these beautiful female antelopes.
Their horns puzzle me, and all of us. They seem to
me as if they were *new* horns, soft and short; time
will prove whether they shed them." He added that
Sprague had made a handsome drawing of the five
young buffaloes that belonged to the fort.

After the launching of the *Union* on August 12,
preparations for the return began in earnest. Audubon hastened to arrange with a half-breed trapper
for more specimens: Bighorns, grizzlies, elk, Black-
tailed Deer, red and gray foxes, badgers, and porcu-

pines. The trapper, François Detaille, was to receive
sums up to ten dollars a head, besides his passage to
Fort Clark as a crewman on the *Union*. He agreed
to guide Audubon on a brief excursion into the Bad
Lands [16] to hunt the Bighorn. Culbertson and
Squires tried to dissuade him from this strenuous
venture, but he firmly refused to abandon it.
"Though my strength is not what it was twenty
years ago," his journal reads, "I am yet equal to
much, and my eyesight is far keener than that of
many a younger man, though that too tells me I am
no longer a youth."

The new barge was ready at last. On August 16
Audubon and his men embarked, taking the painter's live specimens aboard in rude cages: a Rocky
Mountain Deer, a Swift Fox, and a badger, bound
for New York. His journal of the return journey
down the Missouri on this last, most picturesque
quest in behalf of his *Quadrupeds* is among the
most vivid word pictures of the frontier in American literature. Never reprinted since its original
publication by Charles Scribner's Sons in 1897, his
own account, slightly abridged, describes the homeward voyage:

Diary of the Return Voyage

August 16th, 1843. Started from Fort Union at
12 M. in the Mackinaw barge *Union* . . . Camped at
the foot of a high bluff. Good supper of Chickens
and Ducks.

17th. . . . Saw three Bighorns, some Antelopes . . .
many Deer . . . one Wolf, twenty-two Swans . . . Elk
. . . Camped at Buffalo Bluff, where we found Bear
tracks.

18th. . . . Bell shot a superb male Elk . . . Stopped
to make an oar, when I caught four catfish . . . Fifteen to twenty female Elks drinking, tried to approach them, but they broke and ran . . . We landed
and pursued them . . .

19th. Wolves howling, and bulls roaring, just like
the long continued roll of a hundred drums. Saw
large gangs of Buffaloes walking along the river . . .
Fresh signs of Indians, burning wood embers, etc.
. . . Abundance of bear tracks. Saw bushes bearing
the berries of which Mrs. Culbertson has given me a
necklace . . .

---

[16] The text for the Bighorn, page 196, describes the Bad Lands.

COTTONTAIL RABBIT. Detail of Fig. 70, page 139, facsimile size. From the original water color in the Pierpont Morgan Library. The legend on the back reads: "I drew this Hare [rabbit] during one of the days of deepest sorrow I have felt in my life, and my only solace was derived from my Labour. This morning our beloved Daughter Eliza died at 2 o'clock. She is now in Heaven, and May our God for ever bless her Soul"

J.J.A.

TEXAS BLACK-TAILED JACK "RABBIT" (*above*). Original study for Fig. 69, page 138. Water color. Size of nature. (City Art Museum of St. Louis, Mo.) PENNANT'S MARTEN (*below*). Prepared for the *Quadrupeds* but never lithographed. Water color. 18″ x 31″. New York, 1841. (Collection of Henry E. Schnakenberg; photograph: Wadsworth Atheneum, Hartford, Conn.)

J.J.A.

YOUNG RACCOON (*above*). Water color. Size of nature. Signed and dated "Young Raccoon of this year, Sept. 1841." Lithographed in octavo edition only, being added to Plate LXI (Fig. 24). (The American Museum of Natural History) ARCTIC HARE (*below*). In winter and summer pelage. The figure at the right was used for Fig. 62, page 132. Among the Audubon originals recently discovered in Sydney, Australia. Water color. 3′ x 30″.

62 1526 196

J.J.A.

ESKIMO DOG

Head detail from Fig. 13. The full plate is reproduced on page 90.

20th. . . . Thousands upon thousands of Buffaloes; the roaring of these animals resembles the grunting of hogs . . . Sprague killed one bull, and I made two sketches of it . . .

21st. Buffaloes all over the bars and prairies, and many swimming. The roaring can be heard for miles. The wind stopped us . . . Bear tracks led us to search for those animals, but in vain . . . Collected seeds . . .

22nd. Went hunting Elks . . . Coming back to the boat Sprague saw a Bear . . . the fellow had turned under the high bank.

24th. . . . The fat of our Bear gave us seven bottles of oil. We heard what some thought to be guns, but I believed it to be the falling of the banks. Then the Wolves howled so curiously that it was supposed they were Indian dogs. We went to bed all prepared for action in case of an attack; pistols, knives, etc., but I slept very well, though rather cold.

25th. . . . We passed two Riccaree winter villages. Many Eagles and Peregrine Falcons. . . . Reached the Mandan village; hundreds of Indians swam to us with handkerchiefs tied on their heads like turbans. Our old friend Four Bears met us on the shore; I gave him eight pounds of tobacco. He came on board and went down with us to Fort Clark . . .

26th. A canoe passed us with two men from the *Opposition* . . . The two fellows are afraid of Indians and want to come on board our boat; we have not room for them, but will let them travel with us. Landed for the night, and walked to the top of one of the buttes . . . a fine and extensive view . . . We heard Elks whistling, and saw many Swans. The canoe men camped close to us.

27th. Started early in company with the canoe. Saw four Wolves and six bulls, the latter in a compact group, difficult to attack. They are poor at this season, and the meat very rank, but yet are fresh meat . . . Mrs. Culbertson worked at the parfleche with Golden Eagle feathers; she had killed the bird herself . . . We saw a bull on a sandbar . . . the animal made for our boat and came so close that Mr. Culbertson touched him with a pole, when he turned off and swam across the river, but acted as if

wild or crazy . . . Montcrévier caught a catfish that weighed sixteen pounds, a fine fish, though the smaller ones are better eating.

29th. Heavy wind all night. Bad dreams about my own Lucy . . . Cut a cotton tree to fasten to the boat to break the force of the waves . . . Saw a Muskrat this morning swimming by our barge. Slept on a muddy bar with abundance of mosquitoes.

31st. Fine and calm. Saw large flocks of Ducks, Geese, and Swans . . . Passed Mr. Primeau's winter trading-house; reached Cannon Ball River . . . Saw a Rock Wren . . . Saw the prairie on fire, and signs of Indians . . . Caught fourteen catfish . . .

September 2nd. Went about ten miles . . . stopped, for the gale was so severe. No fresh meat on board. Saw eight Wolves, four white ones. Walked six miles on the prairies, but saw only three bulls . . . Black-breasted Prairie Larks . . . Black Ducks.

3rd. . . . No meat for another day. Stopped for the night at the mouth of the Moreau River. Wild pigeons, Sandpipers, but no fish.

4th. Stopped by the wind at eleven . . . Found Beaver tracks, and small trees cut down by them. Provost followed the bank and found their lodge, an old one . . . Mr. Culbertson killed a buck, and we have sent men to bring it entire. It is skinned and in brine . . . Provost and I went to set traps for Beaver . . .

5th. . . . Nothing caught . . . We saw a Pigeon Hawk giving chase to a Spotted Sandpiper on the wing, which dove under water and escaped . . . Met Harris, and started a monstrous Elk from its couch in a bunch of willows; shot at it about eighty yards off, but it was not touched . . . We yet hope to get this fine animal. Harris found a Dove's nest with one young one, and an egg just cracked by the bird inside; the nest was on the ground. Curious all this, at this late season, and in a woody part of the country. Saw a bat.

7th. About eleven last night the wind shifted *suddenly* to northwest, and blew so violently that we all left the boat in a hurry. Mrs. Culbertson, with her child in her arms, made for the willows and had a shelter for her babe in a few minutes. Our guns and ammunition were brought on shore, as we were afraid of our boat sinking. We returned on board after a while; but I could not sleep, the motion making me very seasick; I went back to the shore and lay down after mending our fire . . . A second gale arose; . . . we removed our boat to a more secure position . . . The birds are now travelling south . . . The river has suddenly risen two feet . . . About ten o'clock Harris called me to hear the notes of the new Whip-poor-will . . . "Oh-will, oh-will" [*Phalaenoptilus nuttalli*] . . . The night was beautiful but cold.

8th. . . . The effect of sudden rises in this river is wonderful upon the sand-bars . . . They at once break up, causing very high waves to run, through which no small boat could pass without imminent danger . . . The current very strong; but we reached Fort Pierre at half-past five . . .

9th. Exchanged our boat for a larger one. Orders found here obliged Mr. Culbertson to leave us and go to the Platte River establishment, much to my regret.

10th. Mr. Culbertson gave me a parfleche [Buffalo bull's hide used for wallets, pouches, etc., now on exhibition at the American Museum of Natural History, New York] which had been presented to him by "L'Ours de Fer," the Sioux chief. It is very curiously painted, and is a record of a victory of the Sioux over their enemies, the Gros Ventres. Two rows of horses with Indians dressed in full war rig are rushing onwards; small black marks everywhere represent the horse tracks; round green marks are shields thrown away by the enemy in their flight, and red spots on the horses, like wafers, denote wounds.

11th. The men are at work, fitting up our new boat.

13th. Our boat is getting into travelling shape. I did several drawings of objects in and about the fort.

14th. We started at two this afternoon; landed at the farm belonging to the fort and procured a few potatoes, some corn, and a pig.

15th. Reached Fort George.

16th. Started early . . . Bell heard Parrakeets . . . Found a Common Meadow Mouse. Landed at the Great Bend for Blacktailed Deer and wood . . . Collected the Yucca plant.

17th. Hard gale last night with rain . . . This morning was beautiful . . . Saw ten or twelve Antelopes on the prairie . . .

18th. Saw a Fish Hawk, two Gulls, two White-headed Eagles, Golden Plovers. Stopped, the wind was so high, and warmed some coffee. Many dead Buffaloes are in the ravines and on the prairies. Sprague outlined a curious hill. Saw Say's Flycatcher, a Grosbeak, the common Titlark. Landed at sunset. Signs of Indians. Wolves howling, and found one dead . . . too far gone to be skinned; I was sorry, as it was a beautiful gray one. These animals feed on wild plums in great quantities.

20th. Tracks of Wild Cats along the shore . . . Saw immense numbers of Pintailed Ducks . . . Stopped on an island to procure pea-vines for my young Deer . . . Ran on a bar and were delayed nearly half an hour. Shot two Blue-winged Teal.

21st. Landed to examine Burnt Hills. Fresh signs of Indians. Saw many Antelopes and Mule Deer . . . Buffalo bulls . . . We cut some timber for our oars . . .

22nd. We were forced to come to by the wind and the rain. Played cards for a couple of hours. No chance to cook or get hot coffee, on account of the heavy storm. We dropped down a few miles and finally camped till next day in the mud, but managed to make a roaring fire. Wolves howling all about us, and Owls hooting. Still raining heavily. We played cards till nine to kill time. Our boat was a quagmire.

23rd. Five wolves were on a sand-bar very near us. Have made a good run of about sixty miles. We took in three men of the steamer *New Haven* which was fast on the bar. We reached Ponca Island and landed for the night. At dusk the steamer came up, and landed above us. I had the gratification of a letter from Victor and Johnny, of July 22nd.

24th. Saw a wolf on a bar, and a large flock of White Pelicans which we took at first for a keel-boat . . . Stopped by wind. Hunted and shot one Raven, one Turkey Buzzard, and four Wood Ducks. Ripe plums abound, and there are garfish in the creek. Found feathers of the Wild Turkey. Signs of Indians, Elks, and Deer. The men made four new oars.

27th. Many Wood Ducks, and saw Raccoon tracks. Passed the Vermilion River. My Badger got out of his cage last night, and we had to light a candle to secure it. Reached the Fort of Vermilion at twelve . . . We bought two barrels of superb potatoes, two of corn and a good fat cow. For the corn and potatoes I paid no less than $16.

28th. The young man who brought me the calf at Fort George has married a squaw, a handsome girl, and she is here with him . . . Provost and I went hunting, and saw three female Elks, but the order was to shoot only bucks . . . I cannot eat beef after being fed on Buffaloes. I am getting an old man, for this evening I missed my footing on getting into the boat, and bruised my knee and my elbow . . . I cannot have the spring of seventeen.

29th. Nighthawks seen flying. Saw a Long-tailed Squirrel that ran on the shore at the cry of our Badger. Michaux had the boat landed to bring on a superb set of Elk horns he secured last week. Abundance of Geese and Ducks. A heavy gale of wind . . . the motion of the boat was too much for me, so I slipped on shore and with Michaux made a good camp, where we rolled ourselves in our blankets and slept soundly.

October 1st. Had several showers. Passed the Big Sioux River . . . Heard a Pileated Woodpecker, and saw Fish Crows. Landed to shoot Turkeys . . . These will keep us going some days . . . Camped at the mouth of the Omaha River, six miles from the village. The wild Geese are innumerable. The wind has ceased and stars are shining.

2nd. Beautiful but *cold.* The water has risen nine inches, and we travel well. Stopped by the wind at a vile place, but plenty of Jerusalem artichokes, which we tried and found very good . . . Made our supper from excellent young Geese.

3rd. A beautiful, calm morning; we started early. Saw three Deer on the bank. A Prairie Wolf traveled on the shore beside us for a long time before he found a place to get up on the prairie . . . Saw more Deer, another Wolf, two Swans, several Pelicans . . . We were caught by a snag that scraped and tore us a little. Had we been two feet nearer, it would have ruined our barge. We passed through a very swift cut-off, most difficult of entrance. We have run eighty-two miles and encamped near the bluffs . . . The Geese and Ducks are abundant beyond description. Bragg, Harris' dog, stole and hid all the meat that had been cooked for our supper.

5th. Blew hard all night, but a clear and beautiful sunrise . . . Reached Fort Croghan about half-past four . . . We were presented with some green corn, and had quantity of bread made, also bought thirteen eggs from an Indian for twenty-five cents. Honey bees are found here, and do well, but none are seen above this place . . .

6th. Our man Michaux was passed over to the officer's boat, to steer them down to Fort Leavenworth, but we are to keep in company, and he is to cook for us at night. The whole station here is broken up, and Captain Burgwin leaves by land with dragoons, horses, etc. Stopped at Belle Vue at nine, and had a kind reception; bought 6 lbs. coffee, 13 eggs, 2 lbs. butter, and some black pepper. Abundance of Indians, of four different nations . . . Passed the Platte and its hundreds of snags . . . The stream quite full, and we saw some squaws on the bar, the village was in sight. Encamped about thirty miles below Fort Croghan. Lieutenant Carleton supped with us and we had a rubber of whist.

7th. Started too early, while yet dark, and got on a bar. Passed McPherson's, the first house in the State of Missouri . . . Indian war whoops were heard by Lieutenant Carleton this morning whilst embarking after we left. We encamped at the mouth of Nishne-bottana, a fine, clear stream. Went to the house of

Mr. Beaumont, who has a pretty wife. We made a fine run of sixty or seventy miles.

8th. Stopped twice by the storm, and played cards to relieve the dullness . . . Presented a plate of the *Quadrupeds* to Lieutenant Carleton, and he gave me a fine Black Bear skin, and has promised me a set of Elk horns . . . Saw a remarkably large flock of Geese passing southward.

9th. Bell shot a Gray Squirrel, which was divided and given to my Fox and my Badger. Squires, Carleton, Harris, Bell, and Sprague walked across the Bend to the Black Snake Hills, and killed six Gray Squirrels, four Parrakeets and two Partridges. Bought butter, eggs, and some whiskey for the men; exchanged knives with the lieutenant.

10th. Beautiful morning. Great flocks of Geese and Pelicans . . . Reached Fort Leavenworth . . . most kindly reception . . . Wrote to John Bachman . . .

11th. Received a most welcome present of melons, chickens, bread, and butter from the generous Major Morton. Left at six . . . Game scarce, pawpaws plentiful. Stopped at Madame Chouteau's where I bought three pumpkins. Reached Independence Landing at sundown; have run sixty miles. Found no letters.

13th. Heavy white frost, and very foggy. Ran well. Tried to buy butter at several places, but in vain. At Greenville bought coffee. Passed Grand River; stopped at New Brunswick and bought excellent beef at 2½ cents a pound, but very inferior to Buffalo. Camped at a deserted wood yard, after running between sixty and seventy miles.

14th. Stopped by high wind at twelve. We ran ashore, and I undertook to push the boat afloat, and, undressing for the purpose, got so deep in the mud that I had to spend a much longer time than I desired in the very cold water. Visited two farm houses and bought chickens, eggs and butter . . . At one place we procured corn bread. The squatter visited our boat, and we camped near him. He seemed a good man; was from North Carolina, and had a fine family. Michaux killed two Hutchins Geese, the first

I ever saw in the flesh. Steamer *Lebanon* passed us going downwards, before sunset. Turkeys and Long-tailed Squirrels very abundant.

15th. Passed Chariton River and village, and Glasgow; bought bread, and oats for my Deer . . . Passed Arrow Rock . . . Boonesville, the finest country on this river; Rocheport, six miles below which we encamped, having run sixty miles.

16th. Beautiful autumnal morning, a heavy white frost and no wind. Passed Nashville, Marion . . . Jefferson City . . . the Osage River . . . Ran sixty-one miles. Met the steamer *Satan*, badly steered. Ducks, Geese, everywhere.

17th. Saw two Deer. Passed the Gasconade River . . . landed at Pinckney to buy bread, coffee, etc. Buffaloes have been seen mired, and unable to defend themselves, and the Wolves actually eating their noses while they struggled, but were eventually killed by the Wolves. Passed Washington and encamped.

18th. Fine and calm. Passed Mount Pleasant. Landed at St. Charles . . . Passed the Charbonnière River, and encamped. The steamer *Tobacco Plant* landed on the shore opposite.

19th. A heavy white frost, foggy but calm. Forced by the fog to stop on a bar, but reached St. Louis at three in the afternoon. Unloaded and sent all the things to Nicholas Berthoud's warehouse. Wrote home.

Left St. Louis October 22, in steamer *Nautilus* for Cincinnati.

Home to Minnie's Land

After collecting his belongings in Berthoud's warehouse, Audubon made haste to leave St. Louis. Thanks to a young man who struck up an acquaintance with him during his journey by canal from Pittsburgh to Philadelphia, a vivid impression is left of his appearance—rough in woodsman's attire, yet patrician. His hawklike eyes and erect bearing put the youth in mind of one of the painter's old eagles, "feathered to the heel," as he rose sleepily from beneath a pile of furs and blankets to be introduced by the captain.

The boy at once surrendered his berth to the patriarch of whose fame he was very well aware. Audubon showed him his live animals and portfolio of drawings. At intervals during the several days' journey they left the canal boat to take a brisk walk ahead of it for several miles along the towpath. Seeing a speck in the distance moving along a fence, the naturalist exclaimed, "See! Yonder is a Fox Squirrel." The boy demanded to know how he could tell the species from so far, and Audubon laughed, "Ah, I have an Indian's eye!"

On November 6, 1843, the day he was expected, the family were eagerly waiting his arrival. They had read in the papers how he had been taken for a Dunker, and were therefore not altogether startled by his beard. The entire household including all the children, and his old friend Captain Cummings who now lived in Hudson, were waiting on the wide porch at the hour when they expected the family carriage to return from Harlem with their hero.

Little imagination is required to guess Audubon's emotions at that hour. John had done much planting, as he knew, and increased the poultry yard, and overseen the harvest of their gardens which looked out over the grand sweep of the Hudson and the Palisades from his beautiful wooded hillside. He hungered for a sight of his new young peach trees, his century-old white pines, his hickories, oaks, and chestnuts, his tulip trees and dogwood in their final autumn brilliance on that fine November day; and the rivulet which at the crest of his own hill became a brook and flowed down a gorge into the Hudson. He was eager to see how his tame and caged animals—otter, badger, muskrat, marten, and the rest—were faring. But, if his letters home after his departure are recalled, it is possible to picture him as fairly atremble to see his family—Lucy, on down to the new grandchild born to Caroline and John during his absence.

They were wondering which of the two roads might bring him. As they heard the rumble of wheels they scattered in both possible directions, each hoping to be the first to see him. But Audubon, unable to endure his excitement, had leaped from the carriage at the top of the hill and cut down the steepest part straight to the front piazza. Those who had waited there, Lucy among them, had his first embrace, then the others came running to greet him. He kissed his sons as well as all the ladies, who marveled at his strikingly wild appearance, his curly hair and full beard, and his green double-breasted blanket coat with big fur collar and cuffs. Before he should shave and lose this fine look, John painted his portrait in oils, now in the American Museum of Natural History.

Such was Audubon's last return. Almost at once he settled down to intensive concentration on the *Quadrupeds*.

7

FINAL PUBLICATION

By 1848 the folio of *The Viviparous Quadrupeds of North America* was finished. Collectors should note that the octavo edition credits to J. W. Audubon ten pictures earlier presented in the folio as "drawn from nature by J. J. Audubon." However, the present book follows the artist designations of the octavo, a later, revised publication which credited seventy-eight pictures to the father.

Audubon, who died on January 27, 1851, did not live to see the last two volumes of the text completed, but these drew heavily on his collection of anecdotes and copious notes as well as his Missouri river journal. Bachman, who edited the material, contributed a goodly number of his own descriptions of the habits of the mammals pictured by the Audubons. The frequent references to "the Creator" may, for the most part, be safely attributed to him, although Audubon was also given to making such devout allusions. Almost all of the truly sparkling and readable passages are recognizable as pure if slightly edited Audubon, sometimes by comparison with his *Episodes of Western Life* and the style of his letters, other times by unmistakable signs such as mention of Kentucky, the West, or Minnie's Land. By the same token, references to Charleston and the northern counties of New York point clearly to Bachman as author.

As for what John Woodhouse Audubon contributed to the text, this is no mystery; his Texas journal is quoted, and Bachman identified him as the source wherever he had such responsibility. The fact that Volume One of the text is generally the best because

it was prepared along with Audubon's spirited direction is the answer to those who may feel that Bachman was the prime mover. He complained to his biographer in 1874, the year he died, that he had been "overlooked" by the Audubon heirs in their writings about the artist and his career, saying disappointedly: "I wrote every line which composed the latter volumes of the *Quadrupeds*." [17] Certainly he could claim full credit for scientific data, and much besides, but this man with the motto, "Truth and No Humbug," was perhaps overestimating his part. The latter volumes are also heavily indebted to John Woodhouse, the son, whom Bachman might have included in claiming credit for the latter volumes; indeed these, too, contain numerous passages from Audubon senior's memoranda.

After Audubon's return from the West, Bachman threw himself into the work with such intensity for a few years that his sight was threatened, once by a gunpowder accident, more than once by eyestrain. In the end he had to dictate from his notes to Victor, who went to Charleston to help finish up the text. Before this, however, he experienced such moods of desperation for want of certain books and specimens that when the Audubons, who had no such intention, seemed to ignore his now pathetic, now humorous pleas, he wrote to Edward Harris to intercede. He even threatened to resign. Harris more than once restored peace to their widely separated efforts, which were constantly hampered by distance, the slow communications and frequent steamer mishaps. Bachman, moreover, was none too contented with the results of the Missouri expedi-

---

[17] Charleston Museum Collection.

58

tion, which concerned itself overmuch with buffaloes and large mammalia, in his opinion, at the expense of "the little Marmots, Squirrels and Jumping Mice." It had, for his conservative taste, too much of Culbertson and "his princess brain-eating, horse-straddling squaw," as he expressed it. But he was obliged to pronounce Audubon's accounts of buffalo hunting "first rate."

When he examined the new supply of lithographs for the *Quadrupeds* in the spring of 1844 Bachman's annoyance completely vanished. "They are most beautiful and perfect specimens of the art. I doubt whether there is anything in the world of Natural History like them. I do not believe that there is any man living that can equal them," he wrote.[18] Here was not only a collaborator's opinion but that of one of the country's revered and respected scientists, who, when occasion demanded, could turn the coin and denounce the hasty scientific judgments sometimes made by the Audubon artists. But Audubon's *"brush,"* he always maintained, was "a truth teller."

Bachman visited the painter in 1845, and found him working on a fine water color of "Le Conte's Mouse."[19] His technique had lost none of its brilliance, but a change was becoming visible in Audubon—the old tenacity, the keenness, the familiar drive were missing. Bachman, more than a little sadly, saw that he must confine his good-natured cajoling to John and Victor. John was then preparing for an expedition into Texas to obtain more quadrupeds, an adventure which provided the text with some stimulating passages. The following year, 1846, Audubon, aware that his eye and hand were becoming less sure, withdrew from the work on the letterpress, letting his sons carry on under Bachman's direction. The decision destroyed the artist's will to live, and hastened his decline.

John spent a year and a half in London in 1846–47, painting in the Zoological Gardens and consulting with J. E. Gray, keeper of the museum's zoological collections. A world which has overlooked his talents—the traditional lot, perhaps, of great men's sons—may be interested in Audubon's opinion of his son as a nature painter. In a short life of her father, John Woodhouse Audubon, Maria R. Audubon described her distinguished grandparent's elation on examining an oil sent from Texas for the *Quadrupeds*. "My mother has told me," she said, "that

when the picture of the Cougars came from Texas where my father had painted it, my grandfather's delight knew no bounds. He was beside himself with joy that his 'boy Johnny' could paint a picture he considered so fine. He looked at it from every point, and could not keep quiet, but walked up and down, filled with delight." (See Figs. 6 and 7.)

The question naturally arises, was John the equal of his father at painting mammals? In justice to both it is difficult to answer fairly. Were the answer to be simply yes or no, the father would be the inevitable choice, the man who, to the world, is "Audubon"—as if there were but one, and one only. His genius at capturing animation and the warily alive aspect of wild life is sometimes so startlingly real that it is as if the image were caught fleetingly, momentarily, on paper. Not even Dürer, great sixteenth century German, conveyed this *wild* quality in his incomparable hares and squirrels, though, in their tameness, these possess no less of the mystical and spiritual power of nature. But this contrast is not a bid to place Audubon before that master! Audubon left most of the larger mammals for his son John to portray, concentrating on small rodents —rabbits, marmots, squirrels, and the like. It is doubtful whether anyone, if put to the test, could view all the mammals by both and guess unerringly which of these men did which. Many of the small rodents by John Woodhouse Audubon would certainly be taken for his father's work, and the large ones for Audubon's. The reader is invited to try his own luck at the proper attribution.[20] So difficult is such a test that it leads to the certain conclusion, long overdue, that this son of J. J. Audubon was an American animal painter of the first order, one who, until now, has been completely overshadowed by his father's name and greatness as a bird painter.

John organized an expedition to seek wealth and animals in California in 1849, the year of the Gold Rush. Several of his large company died of cholera along the way. The undertaking was tragically unsuccessful. John returned home overland, leaving some two hundred new drawings and oils for a friend to carry to New York by boat, but the vessel sank with all its passengers and cargo.

The indomitable Madame Lucy Audubon, who lived until 1874, published a life of her husband in 1869, and took up teaching again in her seventieth

---

[18] Charleston Museum Collection.
[19] See Pine Vole, Fig. 115, page 176.

[20] The initials J.J.A. or J.W.A. under the plates denote the work of father or son.

year. But John and Victor, their lives doubtless shortened by their strenuous part in Audubon's plans, did not long survive him. Victor, father of six, died in 1860. John died two years later, leaving a wife and seven children. Due to his relatively lusterless place in the Audubon triumvirate, Victor's name is invariably mentioned last. But his tangible contribution was enormous, as witness an Act of Congress of 1858 whereby a hundred miniature sets of both *Quadrupeds* and *Birds* were presented to the governments of foreign nations. The honor was due in great part to Victor's labors in having, for twelve years, ushered the folio and small editions to the printer Bowen in Philadelphia beginning in 1842, and into the hands of the many subscribers eager to receive them.

This, in brief, is the little known history of Audubon's *Quadrupeds*. The second of his eminently destined scientific works was achieved with all the strength and beauty of his vision.

RICHARDSON'S RED SQUIRREL   Female. Detail from Fig. 86. The full plate is reproduced on page 155.

J.J.A.

J.J.A.

FREE-TAIL BAT. Male (*above*), female (*left*). Inscribed "Drawn from the life!" Water-color drawing. Life size. Two figures on one sheet 19″ x 11¼″. Dated October 29, 1841.

N.B. A group of nine pages of bats by J. J. Audubon and six by J. W. Audubon came to light at The New York Historical Society as this book was about to go to press. The originals were intended for publication but for unknown reasons were never included in either of the original quadruped editions. The drawings on this page are from this group.

RED BAT. Female (*above*), male (*below*). Inscribed "Shot at Hoboken, August 18 and drawn 19th, 1841. *J.J.A.*"

"THE VIVIPAROUS QUADRUPEDS
OF NORTH AMERICA"

SELECTIONS FROM THE TEXT

In the original Imperial folio and Royal octavo editions of *The Viviparous Quadrupeds of North America*, there was no grouping of species. Each plate was inserted in the book as finished. In the present volume, however, general groups of species have been made, any slight departures from common field guide practice occurring where Audubon illustrated different species in one plate, or for reasons of production and appearance of the book. Excerpts from the text in the 1854 miniature edition and other sources follow. Chosen for interest and color, they are abridged and slightly edited. More material was written by the Audubons and Bachman on some mammals than others, which accounts for the varied length of the captions.

Fig. 1. OCELOT *(page 79)*

"The specimen from which our figure was drawn was procured by Colonel Harney seven miles from San Antonio in December, 1845, and sent to John Woodhouse Audubon, then at San Antonio, on an expedition in search of Texas quadrupeds for our work. Here is an extract from the latter's journal:

"'But for Colonel Harney's kindness I might never have made the drawing of this most beautiful of all the North American feline race. I was invited out to his camp, and as I talked of the animals I was most anxious to obtain, all seemed desirous to aid me. Colonel Harney, fond of field sports, was as active and industrious as he was tall and magnificent looking. He walked the lone prairies and swamps at daylight with shouts of encouragement to his small pack of dogs, till they in turn burst forth in full cry on the hot trail of this handsome specimen—the Ocelot from which my drawing was made. This was a new animal to me, though I knew of its existence, so that my delight was only equalled by my desire to paint a good figure of it. Its beautiful skin makes a most favorite bullet pouch, and its spots are only surpassed by the rich, glossy coat and fur of the far-famed Black Otter.'"

—*Quads. Vol. II, p. 261.*

Fig. 2. COMMON AMERICAN WILD CAT *(page 80)*

"We once, while resting on a log in the woods on the banks of the Wabash river, perceived two Wild Turkey cocks at some distance below us, under the bank near the water, pluming and picking their feathers. Of a sudden one of them flew across the river, and the other we saw struggling in the grasp of a Wild Cat, which almost instantly dragged it up the bank into the woods and made off.

"A 'Cat' that was kept alive at Charleston, and afterwards for a short time at our house in the city of New York, showed its affinity to the domestic cat by purring and mewing at times loud enough to be heard at some distance. In the woods during winter its loud caterwauling can be heard at the distance of a mile.

"We once made an attempt at domesticating one of the young of this species. Only two weeks old, it was a most spiteful, growling and snappish little wretch, and showed no disposition to improve its habits and manners under our kind tuition. We placed it in a wooden box, from which it was constantly striving to gnaw its way out. One night it escaped into our library where it made sad work among the books. We fastened it with a light chain and had a small kennel built for it in the yard. Here it was constantly indulging its carnivorous propensities, and catching the young poultry, which it enticed within its reach by leaving a portion of food at the door of its house, into which it retreated until an opportunity offered to pounce on its unsuspecting prey."

—*Quads. Vol I, pp. 12–13, 14.*

Fig. 3. CANADA LYNX (page 81)

"When alarmed or pursued, the Canada Lynx leaps or bounds rapidly from the danger, and takes to a tree if hard pressed by the dogs. It can leap from a considerable height without feeling the jar, alighting on all fours at the same instant, ready for flight or battle.

"The specimen from which we drew the figure was sent to us from Halifax, Nova Scotia. It had been taken in a wolf-trap, after having destroyed several sheep. We kept it alive, feeding it on fresh raw meat. When a dog approached the cage, the Lynx drew back to the farthest corner, and with open jaws spat forth like a cat at the intruder. We often admired the brilliancy of its large eyes when it glared at us.

"The slow multiplication of this species proves that it is not intended to be abundant. There is then a meaning in this arrangement of Providence; and the more we investigate the works of Him who hath created nothing in vain, the more we are led to admire the wisdom of His designs."

—*Quads. Vol. I, pp. 139, 140, 142.*

Fig. 4. TEXAS WILD CAT (page 82)

"The specimen was procured with several others by John Woodhouse Audubon near Castroville, Texas.

"This variety of Lynx may be called the Common Wild Cat of Texas, a wily and audacious predator. Should he be lurking in the dense thicket when the crack of the rifle is heard, and the wild gobbler falls to earth, he will, instead of fleeing at the report of the gun, seize the bird and bear it off at full speed, even if in sight of the enraged and disappointed marksman. In general, however, the Southern Lynx will fly from man's presence. We have known one to be chased from eleven o'clock in the morning till dark night without being treed."

—*Quads. Vol. II, p. 295.*

Fig. 5. JAGUAR (page 83)

"The Jaguar compares with the Asiatic Royal Tiger in size and shape, though its legs are shorter. Of all American animals it is unquestionably the most to be dreaded. Compared with it the Cougar need hardly be dreaded more than the Wild Cat, and the Grizzly Bear is inferior in swiftness and stealthy cunning. During the whole night he is abroad, but is most frequently met with in moonlight and on fine nights, disliking dark and rainy weather, though at the promptings of hunger he will draw near the camp of the traveller, or seek the almost wild horses or cattle of the ranchero in daylight with the coolest audacity.

"At the time that John Woodhouse Audubon was at San Antonio de Bexar in 1845, the Rangers informed him that the Jaguar was most frequently found about the watering places of the mustangs and Deer. It will spring on the former, and from time to time it kills one, but it is much more in the habit of attacking colts about six months old, which it masters with great ease. When lying in wait at the watering place, this savage beast exhibits patience and perseverance, remaining crouched down for hours, with head depressed, still as death. But when some luckless animal approaches, its eyes seem to dilate, its hair bristles, its tail waves back and forth, and all its powerful limbs quiver with excitement. The unsuspecting creature draws near, and suddenly, with a tremendous leap, the Jaguar pounces on him.

"In a conversation with General Sam Houston at Washington city, he informed us that he had found the Jaguar east of the San Jacinto river, and abundantly on the headwaters of some of the Rio Grande's tributaries."

—*Quads. Vol. III, pp. 2, 4–5, 6.*

Figs. 6 and 7. COUGAR (pages 84, 85)

"The male from which our drawing was made was shot in the act of feeding on a black heifer which he had seized, killed and dragged into the edge of a thicket. The Cougar is, however, generally compelled to subsist on small animals or birds. His courage is not great, and unless very hungry, or wounded and at bay, he seldom attacks man.

"The female is a most affectionate mother, and will not leave her young cubs unless occasionally to procure food to support her own strength. She therefore often becomes very lean and poor. The female we have drawn was in this condition. We procured one of her cubs and drew it, presenting its beautiful spots, seldom before noticed. The other cub made its escape. The whelps are suckled by the dam until about half grown, and then they hunt with the old ones (which generally go in pairs) until the mother is with young again, or the young ones find mates.

"A respectable gentleman of the state of Mississippi gave us the following account. A friend of his, a cotton planter, one evening while at tea was startled by a tremendous outcry among his dogs. He ran out to quiet them, thinking that someone had called to see him—perhaps a neighbor. The dogs could not be driven back, but rushed into the house. He drove them all out but one, which ran under the table. He then took a candle, and looking down he was suprised and alarmed to discover that the supposed refractory dog was a Cougar. He retreated swiftly, and the females and children fled, frightened half out of their senses. The Cougar sprang at him, and he parried the blow with the candlestick. But the animal flew at him again, leaping forward perpendicularly, striking at his face with its fore feet and at his body with the hind feet. He repelled these attacks by dealing the Cougar straightforward

blows on its belly with his fist, lightly turning aside and evading its claws as best he could.

"The Cougar had nearly overpowered him when, luckily, he backed toward the fireplace, and as the animal sprang again he dodged him. The panther almost fell into the fire, and was so terrified that he endeavored to escape, darted out the door, and was immediately attacked by the dogs. With their help and a club he was killed.

"Two raftsmen on the Yazoo river, one night encamped on the bank, under a small tent they carried with them, just large enough to cover two. They had a merry supper, and having made a large fire they retired—'turned in,' and were soon fast asleep. The night waned, and by degrees a drizzling rain, followed by a heavy shower, half wakened one of them, when of a sudden he heard the savage growl of a Cougar. In an instant the animal pounced on the tent and overthrew it, and the impetus of the Cougar's spring carried it over them. They started up, scuffled out of the tent, and saw the creature facing them by the dim light of the fire, ready for another leap. With haste they seized two burning sticks, and by whirling them around their heads with loud whoops they scared away the midnight prowler. They did not, however, try to sleep in their tent any more that night after this adventure!

"These instances are very rare, and such tales by frightened travellers must be received with some caution, and with due allowance for man's natural disposition to indulge in the marvelous."

—*Quads. Vol. II, pp. 307, 308–309, 312.*

Fig. 8. COYOTE OR PRAIRIE WOLF (page 86)

"By its predatory and destructive habits this Wolf is a great annoyance to the settlers in the new territories of the west. Travellers and hunters on the prairies dislike it for killing the deer, which supply these wanderers with their best meals, and furnish them with part of their clothing, the buck-skin breeches, the most durable garment, for the woods or plains. The bark or call-note of this Wolf is sometimes welcomed, as it often announces the near approach of daylight. And if the wanderer, aroused from his slumbers by the howling of this animal, raises his blanket and turns his head toward the east, from his camping ground underneath the branches of some broad spreading live-oak, he can see the red glow that fringes the misty morning vapors, giving the promise of a clear and calm sunrise in the mild climate of Texas, even in the depth of winter. Should daylight thus be at hand, the true hunter is at once afoot, and soon he has made a fire, boiled his coffee, and broiled a bit of venison or Wild Turkey."

—*Quads. Vol. II, p. 153.*

Fig. 9. TEXAS RED WOLF *(page 87)*

"We have represented a fine specimen of this Wolf on a sand-bar, snuffing at the bone of a buffalo, which, alas! is the only fragment of 'animal matter' he has in prospect for breakfast.

"An extract from the Texas journal of John Woodhouse Audubon gives us a bit of an adventure with a hungry one, experienced by one of the gallant Texas rangers: 'I was out on a survey about fifteen miles west of Austin, in a range that we didn't care about shooting in any more than we could help, for the Comanche Indians were all over the country. Having killed a Deer in the morning, I took the ribs off one side, wrapped them in a piece of the skin, tied it to my saddle and carried it all day to have it for supper. It was a dark dismal day and I was cold and hungry when I got to where I was to camp. I made my fire, for it was now dark, and with two sticks put up my precious Deer ribs to roast. I walked off to rub down my horse while they were cooking. I heard a stick crack. That means something in Indian country. I turned and saw a large Red Wolf actually stealing my ribs as they roasted. Instinct made me draw a pistol and "let drive" at him. The smoke came in my face and I saw nothing but that my whole supper was gone. I lay down, supperless, on my blanket. At daylight I was up to look out for my breakfast, and to my surprise my half-cooked ribs lay within twenty feet of the fire, and the Wolf about twenty yards off—dead—my ball having been as well aimed as if in broad daylight.' "

—*Quads. Vol. II, pp. 241–242.*

Fig. 10. RED WOLF *(page 88)*

"Wolves of this color were abundant near Henderson, Kentucky, when we removed to that place, and we saw them frequently during our rambles through the woods after birds. We found a Black Wolf [color phase of Red Wolf] in one of our Wild Turkey pens early one morning.

"Once when we were travelling on foot not far from the southern boundary of Kentucky, we fell in with a Black Wolf following a man with a rifle on his shoulders. The man assured us it was as gentle as any dog, and that he had never met with a dog that could trail a Deer better. We were so much struck with this and the Wolf's noble appearance that we offered a hundred dollars for it, but the owner would not part with it for any price.

"Our plate was drawn from a fine specimen, although not so black a one as we have seen."

—*Quads. Vol. II, pp. 127, 130.*

Fig. 11. GRAY WOLF *(page 88)*

"When we reached Fort Union in the Missouri country in 1843 we found Wolves in abundance, but the White Wolf was far the most common. We arrived on June 12th, and soon after our arrival, Mr. Culbertson who was head of the post told us that if a Wolf made its appearance on the prairie near the Fort, he would give chase on horseback and bring it back to us alive or dead. Shortly afterward a Wolf came in view, and in a few moments we saw him on his prancing steed as he rode out of the Fort with gun in hand, attired only in shirt, breeches and boots. He spurred his horse and went off with the swiftness of a jockey. The Wolf trotted off and every now and then stopped to gaze at the horse and rider, but finding he could not safely indulge his curiosity he suddenly galloped off with all his speed. The steed began to gain on the poor cur; and as a signal to us that he felt sure of bringing in the beast, he fired off his gun. The fugitive gained the hills beyond, but he had no time to make for the deep ravines. We heard the crack of the gun again. Mr. Culbertson, galloping along dexterously, picked up the slain Wolf without dismounting, threw it across the pummel of his saddle, wheeled round and rode back to the Fort as fast as he had gone forth. A hard shower of rain was an added motive for his pace, and triumphantly he placed the trophy of his chase at our disposal—all inside of twenty minutes—assuring us that such feats as this capture were so very common that no one considered it worthy of being called an exploit."

—*Quads. Vol. II, pp. 157–158.*

From the Missouri River Journal, July 9, 1843:

"Provost tells me that Wolves are oftentimes destroyed by wild horses, which he has seen run at the Wolves head down, and when at a proper distance take them by the middle of the back with their teeth, and throw them several feet in the air, after which they stamp upon their bodies with the fore feet until quite dead."

Fig. 12. HARE INDIAN DOG (page 89)

"This Dog resembles the Wolf more than the Fox. It is more domestic than many of the Wolf-like dogs of the plains. The Indians north of the Great Lakes use it in hunting, but not as a beast of burden or for draught. We have never had an opportunity to see it, except in the stuffed specimen from which our drawing was made.

"Sir John Richardson says of it: 'Although the Hare Indian Dog is playful and affectionate, it is not very docile, and dislikes confinement. If conscious of deserving punishment it will hover round the tent of its master without coming within his reach, even if he calls it. Its howl, when hurt or afraid, is that of a Wolf. We used mongrel dogs for draught at Fort Franklin, which pursued the Hare Indian Dogs meaning to devour them, but the latter easily escaped them, outstripping them in speed. A young puppy became greatly attached to me, and when about seven months old ran on the snow by the side of my sledge for nine hundred miles without suffering from fatigue. During this march it frequently, of its own accord, carried a small twig or one of my mittens for a mile or two. But it showed little aptitude for learning the arts which the Newfoundland Dogs acquire, such as fetching and carrying.'"

—*Quads. Vol. III, pp. 153, 154.*

Fig. 13. ESKIMO DOG (page 90)

"Our drawing was made from a fine living Dog in the Zoological Garden at London. The animal, as the name imports, is the constant companion of the Esquimaux and is found among various tribes of Indans farther north in the Arctic regions. Our figures do not show these animals as very closely allied to the Wolf; on the contrary, their look of intelligence would indicate that they possess sagacity and aptitude of man's service equal at least to that of many favorite breeds of Dog.

"We found several families of coastal Labrador depending entirely on their Dogs to convey them on visits to their neighbors. Some had packs of forty or more. The fish were so abundant that we could scoop them out of the water with a pocket handkerchief. The Dogs wade in and snap at them with dexterity as the surf retires, eating them alive. If a severe storm on a winter journey delays a team's arrival at a settlement and their food supply gives out, they will devour the driver in their ravenous hunger, and even prey on one another. They are taught to go in harness from the time they are two or three month-old pups, to gain experience and learn to obey their master. They require the strictest discipline to keep them in subjection.

"Captain Lyon reports that seven of his Dogs could run a mile in four minutes, drawing a heavy sledge full of men."

—*Quads. Vol. III, pp. 58, 59, 60.*

Fig. 14. SILVER FOX (page 91)

"It gives us pleasure to render our thanks to the Hudson's Bay Company for a superb female Black or Silver-gray Fox which was procured for us, and sent alive to the Zoological Gardens in London, where John Woodhouse Audubon was then making figures of some of the quadrupeds from the Arctic regions of our continent. Having drawn this beautiful animal which was at the time generously tendered us, but thinking it should remain in the Zoological Gardens, as we have no such establishment in America, J. W. Audubon declined the gift in favor of the Society. When shall we have a Zoological Garden in the United States?

"It is stated by Dr. Morton that the skin of the Black Fox was considered by the Indians of New England as equivalent to forty Beaver skins, and, when offered to and accepted by their kings, it was looked upon as a sacred pledge of reconciliation."

—*Quads. Vol. III, p. 72.*

Fig. 15. RED FOX (page 92)

"We received a beautiful specimen of the Red Fox, in the flesh, from our friend Edward Harris of Moorestown, New Jersey, near Philadelphia, and our figure was drawn from it. We represented the animal just caught in a steel-trap.

"The Red Fox is far more active and enduring than the Gray, and generally runs in a more direct line, so that it always gives both dogs and hunters a good long chase. Where the hounds are not accustomed to follow, it will frequently beat out the whole pack, and the horses and huntsmen to boot... We once knew a Red Fox that had been chased frequently, and always escaped at the same spot, by the hounds losing the track. The secret was at last found out; the Fox always took the same course, running ahead of the dogs so far that they could not see him. He would leap from a fallen log onto a very sloping tree and conceal himself in the branches, and as soon as the dogs passed he ran down and, leaping onto his old track, ran back in his former path. So dexterously was this 'tour' performed that he was not suspected by the hunters.

"To decide whether the speed of the Red Fox was as great in the South as in the colder regions of the North, several gentlemen near Augusta decided to test the question with a chase in 1844. Thirty of them gathered with a hundred hounds at two o'clock on a moonlight morning. They started a Fox which took to open country on the west bank of the Savannah. A number of men were mounted on fleet horses, and one of them rode three hunters in succession during the chase which was kept up in pursuit of the flying beast till three o'clock in the afternoon. After thirteen hours the horses and the whole pack of hounds were broken down and the hunt was abandoned. The Red Fox digs an extensive burrow with two or three openings, to which he retreats after a hard chase and as a last resort.

"The young, from four to six at a birth, are born in February and March. They are born blind and are not seen at the mouth of the den for about six weeks, when the Fox, urged by hunger and instinct, goes out in search of prey for their young."

—*Quads. Vol. II, pp. 265, 267, 269, 270, 271.*

N.B. See long-tailed Red Fox, pages 192, 214.

Fig. 16. CROSS FOX (page 92)

"The specimen for our drawing was caught not far from the falls of Niagara, and was purchased by John Woodhouse Audubon from the proprietor of the 'Museum,' who had kept it to gratify the curiosity of the travellers who visit the great Cataract. It was brought alive to New York.

"In our youth we had opportunities, while residing in northern New York state, of observing the habits of the fox and many other animals abundant around us. We were invited to join several neighbors of the vicinity who vied with one another in destroying foxes, and we did so on a few occasions. But finding that our ideas of sport did not accord precisely with theirs, we gradually withdrew from this club of primitive fox hunters and their dogs, pick-axes and spades."

—*Quads. Vol. I, pp. 51–52.*

Fig. 17. KIT FOX OR SWIFT FOX (page 93)

"The first Swift Fox we ever saw alive was at Fort Clark on the Upper Missouri, where we arrived June 7th, 1843. Mr. Chardon, the principal at the Fort, with great kindness and politeness presented it to us. He assured us that good care would be taken of it during our absence up the river to the base of the Rocky Mountains, and that on our return to the Mandan village we might easily take it with us to New York. Mr. Chardon informed us that this Fox was a most expert rat catcher, and had been kept in a loft without any other food than the rats and mice it caught there. It was a beautiful animal, and ran with great rapidity from one side of the loft to another to avoid us.

"Soon after we left Fort Clark we saw on an open prairie the second Swift Fox met with on our journey. Our party had been shooting buffaloes. Edward Harris, mounted on an Indian horse, had no difficulty in keeping up with it. This slight adventure convinced us that the accounts of the wonderful speed of this animal are considerably exaggerated. Godman states that the fleetest Antelope or Deer is passed by this little Fox, and such is the celerity of its motion that it is compared by the celebrated Lewis and Clark (and by Mr. Say who named it) 'to the flight of a bird.'

"During our homeward journey our Fox, placed in a wooden box lined in part with tin, and with a chain fastened to a collar around its neck, safely reached our residence near New York. We placed it in a large cage box two-thirds beneath the surface of the ground, completely tinned inside and half filled with earth. When thus allowed a comparatively large space and plenty of earth to burrow in, the Fox soon dug a hole large enough to conceal himself entirely."

—*Quads, Vol. II, pp. 15–16.*

Fig. 18. GRAY FOX (page 94)

"The Red Fox is far more to be dreaded than the Gray. The Gray Fox is shy and cowardly, and the snap of a stick or the barking of a dog will set him off at a full run, and he preys on other species weaker than himself. Condemn him not, too hastily. He has a more strikingly carnivorous tooth than yourself, and he takes no wanton pleasure in destroying the bird, exhibits to his companions no trophies of his skill, and is contented with a meal, while you are perhaps not satisfied when your capacious bird-bag is filled.

"As long as the Gray Fox can wind through the thick underbrush, he will seldom resort to a tree, to which he is forced by open woods and a hard chase. In general he digs no burrows and does not conceal himself in the earth. However, we saw one instance to the contrary near Albany. Its kennel is usually in a fallen hollow log, or under the roots of a tree. It is frequently caught in steel-traps, and seems far less cunning than the Red species. We have never, however, seen it taken in box traps; and it is not often caught in dead-falls successful for the Raccoon and Opossum."

—*Quads. Vol. I, pp. 164–165, 167–168.*

Fig. 19. ARCTIC FOX (page 95)

"In winter every part of this Arctic animal is white, except the tip of the nose, the nails and eyes. In spring when the snow begins to disappear it sheds the long white hair and begins to turn brown. It is comparatively unsuspicious and gentle, and less snappish and spiteful than any other Fox even when first captured. It is said that not all the Arctic Foxes turn brown; a pure white one is occasionally met with in the middle of summer, the *Kakkortak* of Greenland.

"Captain Lyon studied these animals on Melville peninsula, and spoke of one caught alive: 'He was small and not perfectly white, but his tameness was so remarkable that I could not bear to kill him. The little animal astonished us very much by his extraordinary sagacity. During the first day, finding himself much tormented by being drawn out repeatedly by his chain, he at length took it up carefully in his mouth whenever he retreated to his hut, and drew it so completely after him that no one who valued his fingers would endeavor to take hold of the end that was attached to the staple.'"

—*Quads. Vol. III, pp. 90, 91, 92, 93.*

Fig. 20. POLAR BEAR (page 96)

"We have journeyed through many a deep dell and wildwood, through swamp and over mountains. We have stemmed the Mississippi's currents, sailed our broad lakes and the seacoast from Labrador to Mexico. We have coursed the huge Buffalo over wide prairies, hunted the timid Deer, trapped the Beaver, caught the Fox. We have, in short, procured, drawn and described many of our animals. Now we will send you with the adventurous navigators of the Polar Seas in search of the White Polar Bear, for we have not seen this remarkable inhabitant of the icy regions. During our Labrador visit in midsummer, 1833, we saw no Polar Bears.

"Many anecdotes are told of accidents to the crews of boats detached from whaling vessels, and by all accounts it appears exceedingly dangerous to attack this animal on the ice. Dr. Scoresby tells us of an impudent attack by a seaman of one of the Hull whalers:

"'The ship was moored to a piece of ice on which, some distance off, a large Bear was prowling about for prey. Emboldened by artificial courage derived from rum, a crewman undertook to pursue it. Armed only with a whale-lance, he resolutely, and against all persuasion, set out on his adventurous exploit over the snow and rugged hummocks until he was within a few yards of the enemy, which, to his surprise, faced him as if inviting him to combat. His courage being by now greatly subdued, partly by evaporation of the stimulus, partly by the threatening aspect of the Bear, he leveled his lance and stopped. The Bear also stood still. The adventurer tried to rally courage for the attack, brandishing his lance and making feints, while the enemy stood his ground. The limbs of the sailor began to quiver as Bruin boldly advanced, extinguishing his last spark of bravery and his dread of ridicule. His flight encouraged the Bear to pursue, and, being more practised at snow travelling, he rapidly gained upon the fugitive. The whale-lance, the sailor's only defense, encumbering his retreat, was thrown down, fortunately exciting the Bear's attention long enough for him to stop and paw it. But again he was at the heels of the panting seaman who dropped one of his mittens to distract him. While Bruin again stopped, the sailor made considerable progress, but the Bear came on again with such perseverance that he dropped another mitten, then a hat, which the creature tore to shreds between paws and teeth. Now rapidly losing strength, the adventurer might have met the fate of his garments had not his shipmates, watching the affair, sallied out to his rescue, the little phalanx opening a passage for him until he reached the shelter of his ship. The Bear came to a standstill, seeming to survey his enemies like an experienced general. Finding them too numerous for hope of his success, he very wisely wheeled about in safe and honorable retreat.'"

—*Quads. Vol. II, pp. 283, 288–289.*

Fig. 21. GRIZZLY BEAR (page 97)

"The Indians consider the slaughter of a Grizzly Bear a feat second only to scalping an enemy. Necklaces of the claws of this beast are worn as trophies among them.

"The audacity of these Bears around Fort Union was remarkable. The waiter, Jean Baptiste, who had been in the company's employ for upwards of twenty years, was picking peas in the garden one day. As he neared the end of the rows he saw a large Grizzly Bear gathering that excellent vegetable also, whereupon he himself dropped his bucket, peas and all, and fled to the Fort. Immediately the hunters turned out on their best horses, and by riding in a circle formed a line which enabled them to approach the Bear on all sides. Finding the animal still greedily feasting on the peas, they shot him without his apparently knowing of their approach. We need hardly say the bucket was empty . . .

"J. W. Audubon wrote in his California journal of 1849–50:

"'High up on the San Joaquin's waters, many of these animals have been killed by the gold miners now overrunning all the country west of the Sierra Nevada. Greatly as it is dreaded, it is hunted with all the more enthusiasm by these fearless pioneers in the land of gold, who have been living for months on salt pork or dry and tasteless Deer meat. I saw many cubs at San Francisco, Sacramento city, and Stockton, and even those no larger than a dog showed evidence of their future fierceness. The beautiful skins make a first rate bed under the thin, worn blanket of the gold digger.'"

—*Quads. Vol. III, pp. 143, 146, 149.*

Fig. 22. AMERICAN BLACK BEAR (page 98)

"We were once enjoying a fine autumnal afternoon on the shores of the beautiful Ohio, with two acquaintances who went along, in quest of some swallows nesting in a high sandy bank, when we observed three hunters vigorously rowing their skiff in the middle of the river. They were pursuing a Bear about a hundred and fifty yards ahead of them, which was cleaving the water as he made for the shore directly opposite us. We rushed down to the water, and launching a skiff we kept for fishing, we hastily put off to intercept the animal. Both boats were nearing the Bear. We, standing in the bow of our skiff, commenced the attack by discharging a pistol at his head. He raised a paw, brushed it across his forehead, and then redoubled his efforts. Repeated shots from both boats were fired at him. We ran alongside, thinking to haul his carcass triumphantly on board, when suddenly, to our dismay, he laid both paws on the gunwale, and his great weight brought the side under water for an instant. We expected the boat would fill and sink. There was no time to lose: we all threw our weight on the other side to counterpoise that of the Bear, and began a pell-mell battery against him with the oars and a boat-hook.

"The men in the other boat also attacked him, and driving the bow of their skiff close to his head one of them killed him with an axe. . . . Tying a rope around his neck, we towed him ashore behind our boats."

—*Quads. Vol. III, pp. 193–194.*

Fig. 23. CINNAMON BEAR [*Local Name for Black Bear*] *(page 99)*

"Our figures were made from living specimens in the gardens of the Zoological Society of London. The Cinnamon Bear has long been known to trappers and fur traders, and its skin is much more valuable than that of the Black Bear. We have given a figure, not because we felt disposed to elevate it to a species, but because it is a variety so frequently found in the collections of skins made by our fur companies, and so often noticed by travellers in the Northwest, that errors might be made by future naturalists were we to omit mentioning it and placing it where it should be."

—*Quads. Vol. III, pp. 126, 127.*

Fig. 24. EASTERN RACCOON *(page 100)*

"The Raccoon is a cunning animal, easily tamed, and it makes a pleasant monkey-like pet. It is quite dextrous in the use of its forefeet and will amble after its master in the manner of a Bear, and even follow him into the streets. It will adroitly pick its keeper's pockets, and is always on the watch for dainties. The habits of the mussels (*Unios*) of our fresh water rivers are better known to the Raccoon than to most conchologists. He invades the nest of the Woodpecker. He watches too the soft-shelled Turtle when she is about to deposit her eggs, for which purpose she leaves the water, crawls onto the white sandbar, digs a hole and places them underneath the heated surface. Quickly does the rogue dig up the elastic ova, and appropriate them to his own use, notwithstanding the efforts of the luckless Turtle to conceal them.

"The specimen from which the large figure on our plate was taken was a remarkably fine male, sent to us alive by our friend the late Dr. John Wright of Troy, New York."

—*Quads. Vol. II, pp. 76, 81.*
N.B. See Crab-eating Raccoon, pages 192, 214.

Fig. 25. RING-TAILED CAT *(page 101)*

"The first impression made by this little animal is that he has met with a little Fox. Ears, sharp nose and cunning look are all foxlike, but its long and movable muzzle approaches the Civets, Genets, and and Coatis. It is lively, playful and nimble, and leaps about on the trees, resembling the Squirrel in agility and grace, always having a hole in the tree where it resides.

"We were only able to take about half a dozen of these shy, retiring animals during our stay in Texas, and not a single female.

"When scolding an intruder the Bassaris (or Ring-tailed Raccoon, as the Texans call it) holds its tail over its back and bends it Squirrel fashion, though it does not stand on its hind feet like the Squirrel, and cannot jump or leap so far. Notwithstanding its shyness it is easily tamed, and is frequently let loose in the houses of the Mexican, catching mice and rats. We have seen such a one running about the streets of a little Mexican village. And we were informed that one was kept as a great pet in a Comanche camp visited by the Indian who hunted for us during our explorations of western Texas."

—*Quads. Vol. II, pp. 314–315, 316, 317–318*

Fig. 26. BLACK-FOOTED FERRET *(page 102)*

"With great pleasure we introduce this new species, procured by a friend on the lower waters of the Platte river in the wooded part of the Rockies, and perhaps beyond, although not observed by any travellers, from Lewis and Clark to the present day. We must hope that private enterprise will gradually unfold the zoological, botanical and mineral wealth of the immense territories we own but do not yet occupy.

"The specimen from which we made our drawing was received by us from J. G. Bell, to whom it was forwarded from the outskirts or outposts of the fur traders on the Platte by Mr. Culbertson. It was stuffed with the wormwood so abundant in parts of that country. We are not aware that another specimen exists in any cabinet."

—*Quads. Vol. II, pp. 298–299.*

Fig. 27. AMERICAN MARTEN (page 102)

"Take a share of the cunning, sneaking character of the Fox, the wide-awake, cautious habits of the Weasel, the voracity of the Mink, add some of the climbing propensities of the Raccoon, and we have a tolerable idea of this little prowler. We have had several specimens sent to us by friends in New York state and the wilder portions of our Canada frontier, from among the woody hills of those districts."

—*Quads. Vol. III, pp. 177, 178.*

Fig. 28. PENNANT'S MARTEN OR FISHER (page 103)

"A servant once came to us before daylight, asking us to shoot a Raccoon for him. After having been chased by his dogs it had taken to so large a tree that he neither felt disposed to climb it nor to cut it down. We soon perceived that instead of a Raccoon the animal was a far more rare and interesting species, a Fisher. We did not shoot, but teased him by shaking some grape vines. He not only became thoroughly frightened but seemed furious. He leaped from branch to branch, showing his teeth and growling. Now and then he ran half way down the trunk, elevating his back in the manner of an angry cat. The servant who had traced him said he appeared to have far less speed than a fox.

"The specimen from which the figure on our plate was drawn was taken alive in the Allegheny Mountains in Pennsylvania, by Spencer Baird of Carlisle. It was voracious, spiteful, growling and spitting, but did not appear to suffer much from captivity. It grew fat, being better supplied with food than in the woods.

"We have seen many skins from the Upper Missouri. The Fisher is enumerated by Lewis and Clarke as one of the species on the Pacific Ocean, in the vicinity of the Columbia River."

—*Quads. Vol. I, pp. 310, 312, 314.*

Fig. 29. BONAPARTE WEASEL (page 104)

"We caught one of these little animals in winter forty years ago in northern New York, in a box trap set near its hole in a pine forest. Supposing it to be a young Ermine we kept it, under the impression that it would become tame and increase in size. But it continued to be wild and cross, concealing itself in its nest during the whole day, and rattling and gnawing at the wires at night to effect its escape. We placed a common Weasel twice its size in with it, and it immediately attacked our little fellow. Towards spring we placed a Norway Rat in its cage to test the Weasel's courage. They retreated to opposite corners and eyed each other during the entire day. Next morning we found the rat had been killed.

"The specimens from which we drew our figures were given us by J. G. Bell, who took them in Rockland County, New York."

—*Quads. Vol. III, pp. 185–186.*

Fig. 30. BONAPARTE WEASEL (page 104)

"Our specimen was captured on Long Island in May, 1834, and is in summer pelage. We find from our notes that in the state of New York, in the winter of 1808, we kept a Weasel which we suppose may have been of this species, together with several young Ermines. The latter all became whiter in winter, but the former underwent no change in color, remaining brown."

—*Quads. Vol. III, pp. 235, 236.*

Fig. 31. LEAST, OR PYGMY, WEASEL (page 104)

"The specimens were obtained in the state of New York, one in the Catskills, the other on Long Island."

—*Quads. Vol. II, p. 101.*

Fig. 32. BRIDLED WEASEL (page 105)

"This species resembles the Ermine. The specimen from which our figure was made was captured by John K. Townsend."

—*Quads. Vol. II, p. 72.*

Fig. 33. NEW YORK WEASEL (page 105)

"In summer the upper body is of a chestnut brown color, in winter snowy white. The name of Ermine is associated with the pride of state and luxury, it being the favorite ornament of the robes of princes, judges and prelates. Its snowy whiteness is emblematic of the purity they *ought* to possess.

"On a winter day when the earth is covered with a broad sheet of snow, our attention has been arrested by this strikingly beautiful little animal peering out from a log heap, or the crevices of a stone fence, its eyes like sapphires. Graceful, rapid, of untiring industry, he is a brave and fearless little fellow. He permits us to approach him to within a few feet, then suddenly withdraws his head. We remain still, and he once more returns, watching curiously our every motion. Yet this little Weasel is fierce and blood-thirsty, possessing an intuitive propensity for destroying every animal and bird within its reach, some of which, such as the Rabbit, the Ruffed Grouse and domestic fowl, are ten times its size. Notwithstanding its destructive habits, it is doubtful whether the Ermine is not rather a benefactor than an enemy of the farmer, ridding his granaries and fields of many depredators. A mission appears to have been assigned it by Providence to lessen the rapidly multiplying number of mice and the smaller rodentia."

—*Quads. Vol. II, pp. 57, 58, 59.*

Fig. 34. AMERICAN MINK (page 106)

"Next to the Ermine, the Mink is the most active and destructive little depredator that prowls around the farmyard, or the farmer's duck pond. The vigilant farmer may see a fine fowl in the clutches of a Mink moving towards a fissure in a rock or a hole in some pile of stones, in the gray of the morning.

"The Mink, when taken young, becomes very gentle. Richardson saw one in the 'possession of a Canadian woman that passed the day in her pocket, looking out occasionally when its attention was roused by any unusual noise.' We had a pet of this kind for eighteen months. It regularly visited an adjoining fish pond morning and evening, and returned to the house of its own accord. It waged war on the Norway Rats in the dam, and caught frogs on the banks of the pond. It never attacked the poultry, and was on good terms with the dogs and cats. Though rather dull at midday, it was very active and playful in the morning and evening and at night. It was fond of squatting in the chimney-corner, and formed a particular attachment to an arm-chair in our study.

"We were familiar with the ways of this Mink in early life, and frequently caught it in traps on the banks of a brook which in those days abounded with trout, suckers and perch. On this sparkling stream we passed many an hour. We found the nest of the animal under the roots of a large tree, where the young were brought forth, and we frequently saw the old ones with fish in their mouths. They swim and dive with ease, but we generally saw them on the ground. We saw four young in the nest on two occasions. We have seen it in the Pennsylvania mountains, northern New York, Vermont, Canada and on the Missouri river journey.

"When we were residing at Henderson, on the banks of the Ohio river, Minks were quite abundant."

—*Quads. Vol. I, pp. 253–254, 258–259,*
Vol. III, pp. 105, 106.

N.B. See also page 192.

Figs. 35 and 36. CANADA OTTER (pages 107, 108)

"One morning we noticed that some of these animals repaired to the root of a large tree on the opposite side of the pond. After a fatiguing walk through the tangled cane-brake and thick underwood of this lonely place, we reached the side near the large tree. Several of the Otters made off at our approach. On sounding the tree with the butt of our gun, we discovered it was hollow. We climbed up to a broken branch from which an opening into the upper part of the hollow enabled us to examine the interior. At the bottom there was quite a large space or chamber to which the Otters retired, but whether for security or to sleep we could not decide.

"Next morning we returned, stopped up the entrance under the water as noiselessly as possible, cut a hole in the side of the tree four or five feet from the ground, peeped in, and discovered three Otters on a sort of bed composed of the inner bark of trees and other soft substances. We continued cutting the hole larger, and when it was sufficiently widened we took some green saplings, split them at the butt-end, and managed to fix the head of each animal firmly to the ground by passing one of these split pieces over his neck. Then we pressed the stick downwards. Our companion then crept into the hollow and we returned home with the Otters.

"This species has a peculiar habit of sliding off the wet sloping banks into the water. The Otters ascend the bank at a place suitable for their diversion. They slide down in rapid succession, and there are many at a sliding place. On one occasion we were resting ourself on the bank of Canoe Creek near Henderson when a pair of Otters appeared, and not seeing our proximity began to enjoy their sliding pastime. They glided down the soap-like muddy surface of the slide with the rapidity of an arrow from a bow, and we counted each one making twenty-two slides before we disturbed their sportive occupation. We are inclined to the belief that this propensity may be traced to those instincts which lead the sexes to their periodical associations.

"The Otter is a very expert swimmer and can overtake almost any fish. When it is shot and killed in the water, it sinks from the weight of its nearly solid and therefore heavy bones. It is, however, usually caught in strong steel-traps. Otters when caught young are easily tamed, and although their gait is ungainly they will follow their owner about, and at times are quite playful. We have twice domesticated the Otter. They became so attached to us that the moment they entered our study they began crawling into our lap—mounting our table, romping among our books and not infrequently upsetting our inkstand and deranging our papers.

"Early writers have told us that the common Otter of Europe had long been taught to catch fish for its owners, and that in the houses of the great in Sweden, these animals were kept for that purpose, and would go out at a signal from the cook, catch fish and bring it into the kitchen for dinner. This is by no means unlikely, except that we doubt the animal's going by itself for the fish. Bewick relates anecdotes of Otters which captured salmon and other fish for their owners.

"Our late friend N. Berthoud of St. Louis told us that while travelling through the interior of Ohio, he stopped at a house where the landlord had four Otters, alive and so gentle that they never failed to come when he whistled for them. When they ap-proached their master they crawled along slowly and with much apparent humility towards him, and looked somewhat like enormous thick and short snakes."

—*Quads. Vol. II, pp. 6–7, 8, 9, 10.*

Fig. 37. SEA OTTER OR SEA BEAVER (page 109)

"Although capable of living almost at sea, this timid and shy creature chiefly resorts to bays, coastal islands, and tide-water rivers, where it can find food but conceal itself as occasion requires. Hunting the Sea Otter was a favorite pursuit of sailors and others around the Bay of San Francisco, until the more attractive search for gold drew them off to the mines when Sutter's mill-race revealed the glittering riches intermixed with its black sand. J. W. Audubon saw one of the hunting shallops at Stockton.

"This animal has been known and hunted for more than a century, and innumerable skins have been carried to China, where they formerly brought a very high price, as well as to Europe."

—*Quads. Vol. III, pp. 172, 175.*

Fig. 38. BADGER (page 110)

"During our stay at Fort Union on the Upper Missouri in the summer of 1843, we purchased a living Badger from a squaw. It had been caught nearly two hundred and fifty miles away, among the Crow Indians. First placed in our common room, it was so mischievous, pulling about and tearing to pieces every article within its reach and trying to dig up the hearth stones, that we moved it into an adjoining room. It managed to dig a hole under the hearth deep enough to conceal its body, and we were obliged to drag it out by main force whenever we wished to examine it. It was provoked at the near approach of anyone and growled continuously at all intruders. It was not, however, very vicious and would suffer one or two of our companions to handle and play with it at times. We concluded to bring it to New York alive, if possible, and succeeded in doing so after much trouble, it having nearly made its escape more than once."

—*Quads. Vol. I, pp. 363–364.*

Fig. 39. WOLVERINE (page 111)

"The Wolverine is one of the animals whose history is blended with superstitions of the old writers, connected with tales of wonder.

"In Denmark, a keeper of a small caravan of animals allowed us the privilege of examining a Wolverine. We took him out of his cage. He was very gentle, opened his mouth to enable us to examine his teeth, and buried his head in our lap while we admired his long claws and felt his wooly feet. He ran round us in circles and made awkward attempts to play with and caress us, which reminded us very much of the habit of the American Black Bear. He had been taught to sit on his haunches and hold a German pipe in his mouth. There was an Alpine Marmot in his cage to which he seemed much attached. Yet he has been called more insatiable and rapacious than the Wolf.

"In the United States the Wolverine has always existed very sparingly and only in the Northern districts. We once obtained one in Rensselaer County on the banks of the Hoosick river.

"Captain Cartwright's Journal records an instance of its strength and cunning: 'In Labrador I crossed the track of a Wolverine which had a trap on one of its feet. As this beast went through the woods where the snow was so deep that I had great difficulty in following him, even in Indian rackets, I was quite puzzled to know how he kept the trap from catching hold of the branches of the trees or from sinking in the snow. But on coming up to him I discovered how he managed, for, after making an attempt to fly at me, he took the trap in his mouth and ran on three legs. These creatures are surprisingly strong in proportion to their size. This one weighed only twenty-six pounds, and the trap eight. Yet, including all the turns he had taken, he had carried the trap six miles.'"

—*Quads. Vol. I, pp. 205, 206–207, 211.*

Fig. 40. LARGE STRIPED SKUNK (page 112)

"There is no quadruped on the continent of North America the approach of which is more generally detested than that of the Skunk. Although from the great and strong we have to apprehend danger, the feeble and apparently insignificant may have it in their power to annoy us almost beyond endurance. Even the bravest of our boasting race is, by this little animal, compelled suddenly to break off his train of thought, *hold his nose,* and run—as if a lion were at his heels!

"Among the first specimens of natural history we attempted to procure was the Skunk, in our early school-boy days. We observed in the path before us a pretty little animal, playful as a kitten, moving quietly along. We pause and gaze; what is it? It is not a puppy or a cat. More gentle than either, it seems desirous to keep company with us, and, like a pet poodle, appears most happy when only a few paces in advance, as if to show the path. What a pretty creature to carry home in our arms! Let us catch it. We run towards it, and it makes no effort to escape, raises its tail as if to invite us to take hold of its brush. We seize it with the energy of a miser clutching a box of diamonds. A short struggle ensues, when—faugh! we are suffocated. We drop our prize and take to our heels, too stubborn to cry, but too much alarmed to take another look at the cause of our misfortune, and undeceived as to the real character of this seemingly mild and playful little fellow.

"We were once requested by a venerable clergyman who had for years been a martyr to violent paroxysms of asthma to procure for him the glands of a Skunk, to be kept tightly corked in a smelling bottle, and to be inhaled when the symptoms appeared. For some time he found relief from his distressing complaint, but he uncorked the bottle on one occasion while in the pulpit. His congregation finding the smell too powerful for their olfactories made a hasty retreat, leaving him nearly alone in the church."

—*Quads. Vol. I, pp. 320, 321, 323.*

Fig. 41. HOG-NOSED SKUNK (page 112)

"A specimen procured by John Woodhouse Audubon in Texas in 1845–46, for the purpose of obtaining a knowledge of the quadrupeds of that country, was caught alive near San Jacinto. It was secured to the pack saddle of one of his baggage mules, but managed to escape during the day's march. As the scent was still strong on the saddle, it was not missed until the party arrived at the rancho

(Continued on page 193)

77

ILLUSTRATIONS

Under the illustrations which follow, all obsolete names of mammals, whether Latin or common, were dropped and correct names furnished by the American Museum of Natural History were substituted. Modern ranges are given. The length—to the root of the tail—is that of actual specimens studied and figured by the Audubons in the original publication. Thumbnail color notes are taken from Audubon's own descriptions. The initials under the plates denote the work of the father (J.J.A.) and the son (J.W.A.). Sex of specimen is the one drawn. Where not specified, no information was given in the original edition. The page reference at the end of each caption denotes the page on which a story about the animal appears.

1. OCELOT, TIGER CAT, SPOTTED CAT, or LEOPARD CAT. Length: 2'11". Color: black-spotted reddish brown. Range: Texas. (Page 65)

Felis pardalis. Male in winter pelage.

J.W.A.

J.J.A.

2. COMMON AMERICAN WILD CAT.
Lynx rufus. Male. Length: 30". Color: yellowish brown with dark brown. Range: central North America; Me. to Ga. (Page 65)

PLATE XVI

3. CANADA LYNX.

Lynx canadensis. Male. Length: 33". Color: generally gray with yellow-brown annulation; dull white undersurface. Range: boreal America—Atlantic to Pacific. (Page 66)

J.J.A.

81

4. TEXAS WILD CAT.
Lynx rufus texensis. Female. Length: 2'5". Color: black-tipped yellowish brown with black spots. Range: Texas and N. M. to Calif. (Page 66)

Felis onca hernandesii. Female. Length: 4'1". Color: buffy yellow; black spots. Range: La., Texas, Mexico. (Page 66)

5. JAGUAR.

J.W.A.

83

J.W.A.

6. COUGAR, PANTHER, PUMA, MOUNTAIN LION, CATAMOUNT.

Felis concolor. Male. Length: 5′1″. Color: tawny. Range: formerly eastern North America from Canadian border to Gulf; now extinct in easternmost part of this region. (Page 67)

Opposite page. Same as above. Female and young. 4′11″.

84

7. COUGAR, PANTHER, PUMA, MOUNTAIN LION, CATAMOUNT.   (Description on opposite page.)

J.W.A.

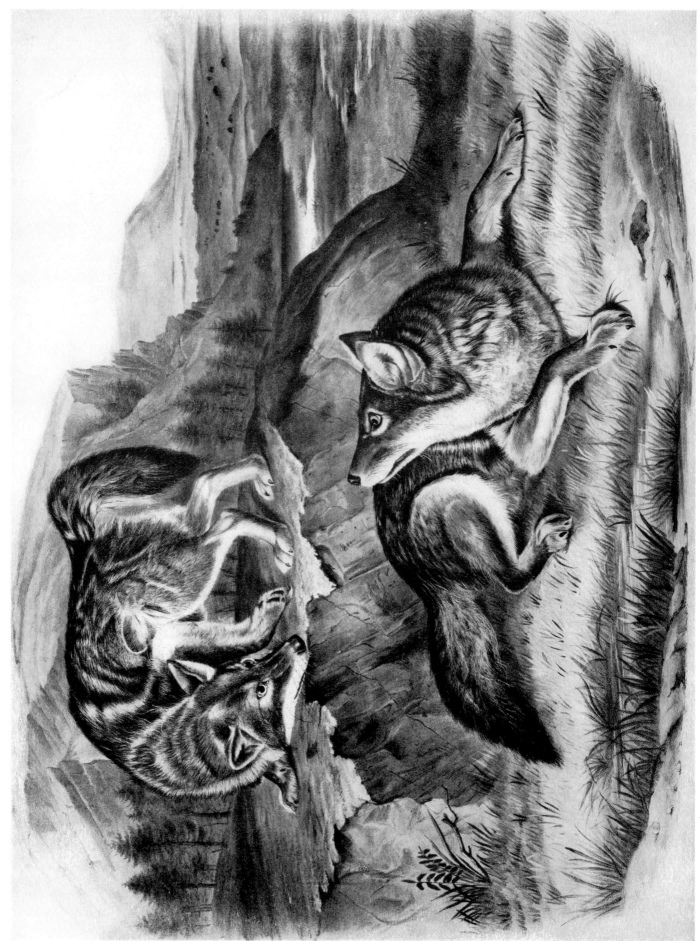

8. COYOTE, PRAIRIE WOLF.

9. TEXAS RED WOLF.   *Canis niger rufus.* Male. Length: 2'11". Color: reddish brown with black patches. Range: Texas and Okla. (Page 68)

J.W.A.

87

10. RED WOLF.

Canis niger gregoryi. Male. Length: 3'2". Color: Audubon's black specimen is a color variety of the species. Range: supposedly extinct east of Mississippi river; formerly Mississippi valley to Ill., Ind., and south through Ky., Tenn., Mo., Ark., La., and Tex. (Page 68)

J.W.A.

11. GRAY WOLF.

Canis lupus. Male. Length: 4'6". Color: white. This specimen is a color phase of the species. Range: North America. (Page 68)

J.W.A.

88

12. HARE INDIAN DOG.

J.W.A.

Canis familiaris. Male. Length: about 3'. Color: white with blackish gray patches. Range: Arctic America. (Page 69)

89

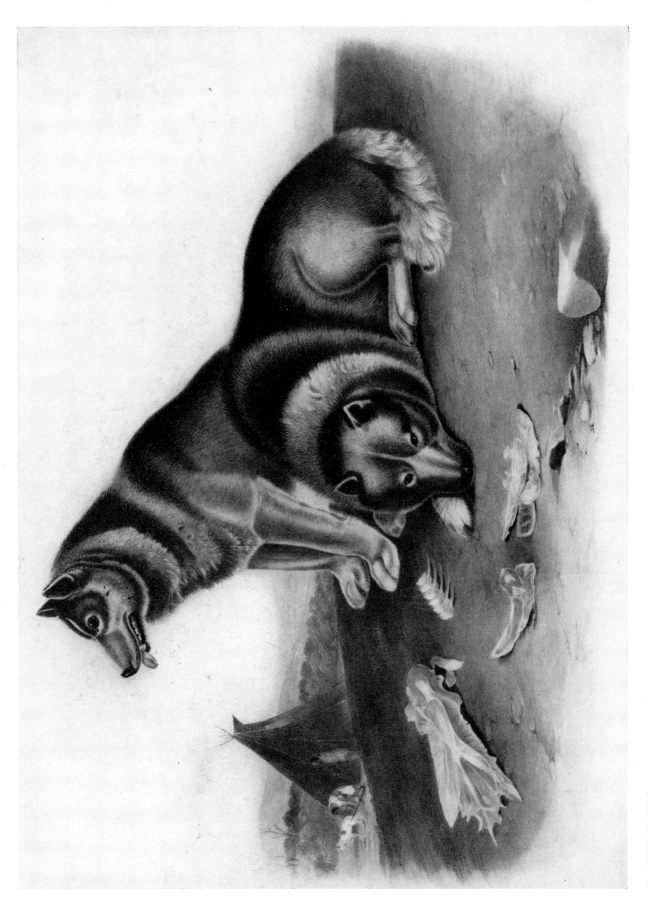

13. ESKIMO DOG. *Canis familiaris.* Males. Length: 4'3". Color: black and yellowish gray. Range: Arctic America. (Page 69) See color detail, page 52.

J.W.A.

14. SILVER FOX.
Vulpes fulva. Female. Length: 2'5". Color phase of the Red Fox. Range: Fox farm industry center is Prince Edward Island, Gulf of St. Lawrence. (Page 69)

J.W.A.

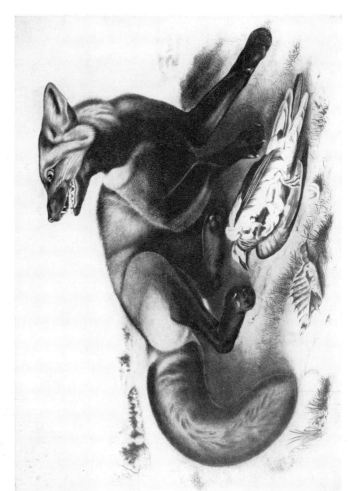

J.J.A.

15 (*left*). RED FOX.

Vulpes fulva. Male. Length: 2'6". Color: red, with white and black areas. Range: N.E. states; introduced into South for hunting. (Page 70)

J.J.A.

16 (*right*). CROSS FOX.

Vulpes fulva. Male. Length: 24¼". Color: dark gray, black-tipped. Cross Fox is a color phase of the Red Fox. Range: N.E. states. (Page 70)

17 (*opposite page*). KIT FOX, SWIFT FOX.

Vulpes velox. Male. Length: 1'8". Color: grizzled brown-black-white; with dull reddish orange; undersurface brownish yellow. Range: Colo. and Neb. plains to Saskatchewan Assiniboia. (Page 70)

17. KIT FOX, SWIFT FOX. (Description on opposite page.)

I.J.A.

18. GRAY FOX
Urocyon cinereoargenteus. Male. Length: 28″. Color: black-tipped gray with brown; sometimes silver-gray. Range: N.Y. and N.J. to Ga., to Mississippi valley north to Ill. (Page 71)

19. ARCTIC FOX, BLUE FOX, WHITE FOX.
Alopex lagopus. Length: 24". Color: *left*, brown with blue tinge (summer); *right*, white (winter). Range: Alaska, Arctic regions. (Page 71)

20. POLAR BEAR.

Thalarctos maritimus. Male. Length: 6'9". Color: white. Range: Arctic regions. (Page 71)

J.W.A.

21. GRIZZLY BEAR.

Ursus horribilis. Males. Length: 5′6″. Color: blackish brown. Range: Wyo. to Alaskan Rockies. (Page 72)

J.W.A.

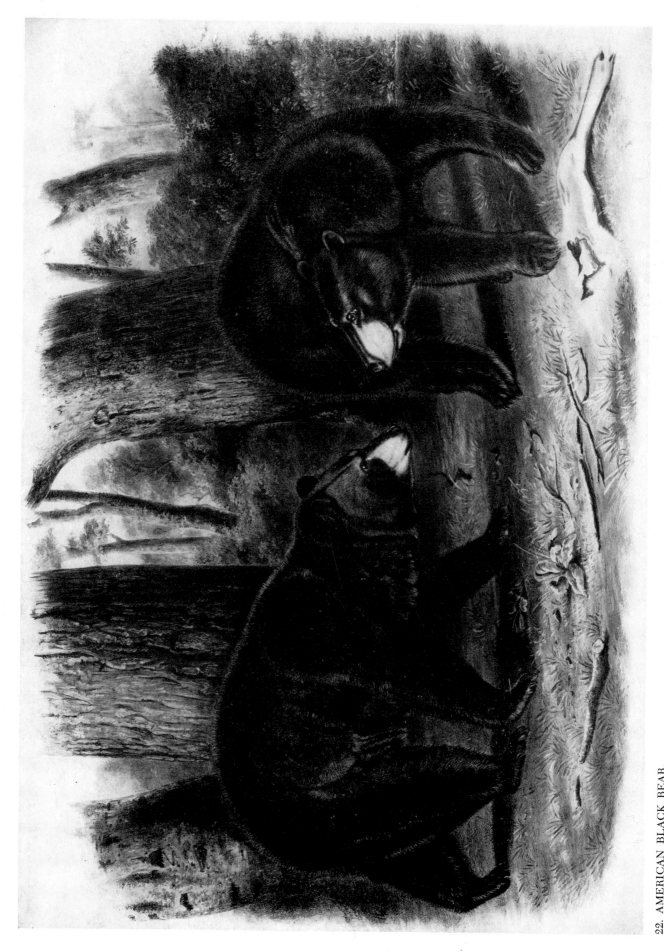

22. AMERICAN BLACK BEAR.
Ursus americanus. Male and female. Length: 6'5". Color: black. Range: wooded North America except La. and Fla., which have other species. (Page 72)

J.W.A.

23. CINNAMON BEAR. *J.W.A.*
Ursus americanus. Male and female. Length: 5'8". "Cinnamon" is a local name for the Black Bear in Alaska and the Rockies, due to its color. Range: same as Black Bear (Fig. 22).
(Page 73)

24. EASTERN RACCOON.

Procyon lotor. Length: 26½″. Color: grizzled gray-brown. Range: eastern Canada to Ga., west to the Rockies north of Texas. (Page 73)

25 (*opposite page*). RING-TAILED CAT, CIVET-CAT, BASSARIS, BASSARISK, RACCOON FOX, MOUNTAIN CAT, CACOMISTLE.

Bassariscus astutus. Male. Length: 1′6″. Color: grayish, with yellow and brown tones, tail black and white. Range: Calif., Texas, Arizona, N.M. (Page 73)

J.W.A.

5. RING-TAILED CAT. (Description on opposite page.)

26. BLACK-FOOTED FERRET. *Putorius nigripes*. Male. Length: 1'7". Color: yellowish brown; black feet, muzzle. Range: Great Plains from N.D. and Mont. to Texas. (Page 73)

27. AMERICAN MARTEN. *Martes americana*. Male and female. Length: 1'5". Color: brown. Range: forested North America from N.Y. to Rockies and northward. (Page 74)

28. PENNANT'S MARTEN, FISHER, PEKAN, BLACK CAT.

Martes pennanti. Male. Length: 23″. Color: chestnut brown with hoary hue. Range: forested North America north of 35° N. lat. (except on Pacific coast, the habitat of the Pacific Fisher). (Page 74)

29. BONAPARTE WEASEL, ERMINE

Mustela erminea cicognanii. Male and female. Length: 8½". Color: white (winter); brown (summer). Range: forested New England and Labrador to S.E. Alaskan coast, south into Rockies and Colo. (Page 74)

J.W.A.

J.W.A.

30. BONAPARTE WEASEL.
(Description on opposite page)

J.W.A.

31. LEAST WEASEL.
(Description on opposite page)

J.J.A.

32. BRIDLED WEASEL.

Mustela frenata frenata. Males. Length: 11″. Color: dark-brownish black; light undersurface. Range: Texas and Mexico. (Page 74)

30 (*opposite page*). BONAPARTE WEASEL, ERMINE (summer pelage). *Mustela erminea cicognanii.* Male. Length: 9″. Color: white (winter); brown (summer). Range: boreal forested North America from New England and Labrador to Alaskan coast; south in Rockies to Colo. from B.C.; common in N.Y., New England, and forested Minn. (Page 74)

31 (*opposite page, bottom*). LEAST WEAS-EL, PYGMY WEASEL. *Mustela rixosa.* Length: 7″. Color: brown; undersurface white. Range: Alaska to Hudson Bay, south to Minn. and Mont. (Page 74)

33. NEW YORK WEASEL.

Mustela noveboracensis. Male and female. Length: 10½″. Color: white (winter); brown (summer). Range: Me., west to Ill. (Page 75)

J.J.A.

34. AMERICAN MINK.   *J.J.A.*

Mustela vison. Male and female. Length: 13″. Color: brown; varies in darkness; white throat. Range: central North America from Canada to Rockies. (Page 75)

35. CANADA OTTER.

Lutra canadensis. Male. Length: 2'7". Color: dark chestnut. Range: wide. (Page 75)

36. CANADA OTTER.

Lutra canadensis. Male. Length: 2'7". Color: dark chestnut. Range: wide. (Page 75)

J.J.A.

J.W.A.

37. SEA OTTER, SEA BEAVER, KALAN.
Enhydra lutris. Male. Length: 4'2". Color: brownish black. Range: nearly extinct; formerly northern Pacific coast to Lower Calif. (Page 76)

109

38. BADGER.
Taxidea taxus. Male. Length: 21". Color: black, white-tipped; brownish in summer. Range: Ind. to Sierra Nevada, south to Kans. and N.M., north to Saskatchewan, lat. 55°. (Page 76)

J.J.A.

39. WOLVERINE.
Gulo luscus. Length: 2'9". Color: blackish brown with reddish brown shoulder and flank. Range: northern U.S. to Arctic regions; Rockies to Colo. (Page 77)

40. LARGE STRIPED SKUNK.

Mephitis mephitis. Female and young. Length: 17". Color: white stripe; blackish brown. Range: wide. (Page 77)

J.J.A.

J.J.A.

41. HOG-NOSED SKUNK, WHITE-BACKED SKUNK.

Conepatus mesoleucus mearnsi. Male. Length: 1'4½". Color: black and white. Range: Texas. (Page 77)

J.W.A.

42. HOODED SKUNK.

Mephitis macroura. Male. Length: 1′4″. Color: black and white. Range: Ariz. and Mexico. (Page 193)

113

43. TEXAS NINE-BANDED ARMADILLO. *Dasypus novemcinctus texanus.* Male. Length: 1½′. Color: brown. Range: Texas and Mexico. (Page 193)

J.W.A.

44. COLLARED PECCARY.   *Pecari angulatus.* Length: 3'4". Color: generally black with gray. Range: Texas and Mexico. (Page 193)

115

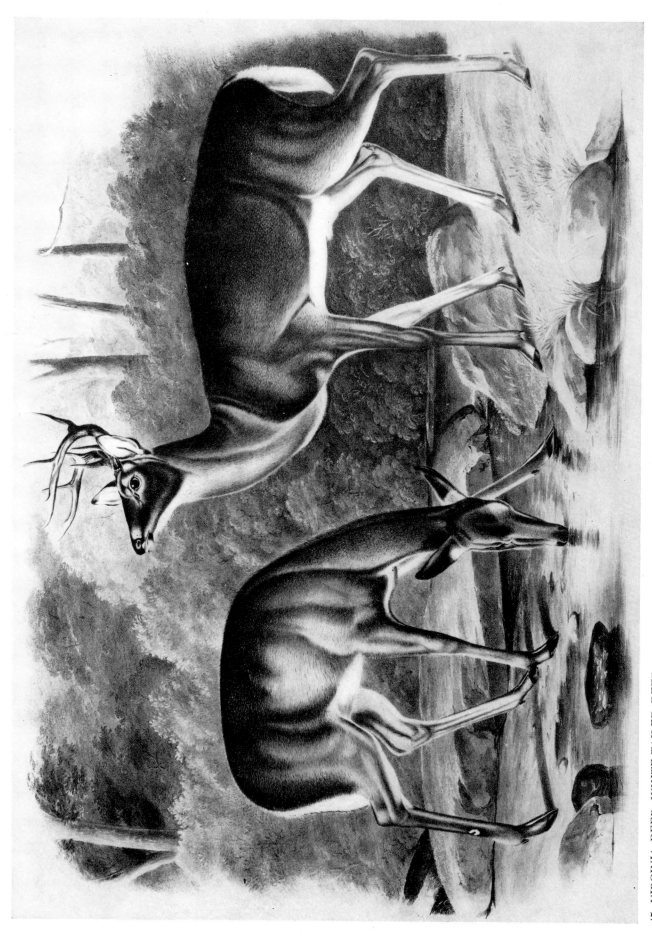

45. VIRGINIA DEER, WHITE-TAILED DEER. *J.W.A.*
Odocoileus virginianus. Male and female. Length: 5'4". Color: brown. Range: Atlantic seaboard to Great Plains, and Gulf to about 43° N. lat. (Page 194)

116

46. VIRGINIA DEER, WHITE-TAILED DEER. *Odocoileus virginianus.* Fawn. [Fig. 45 shows adult male and female.] (Page 194)

J.W.A.

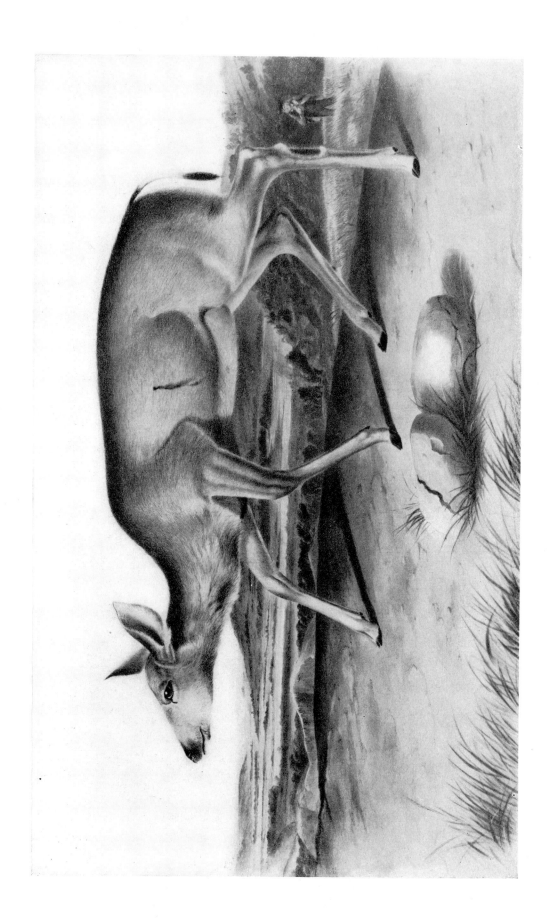

J.W.A.

47. MULE DEER.　　Odocoileus hemionus. Female. Length: 4'10". Color: yellowish brown. Range: Ariz. to B.C. (Page 194)

48. OREGON WHITE-TAILED DEER.

Odocoileus leucurus. Male. Length: 4'2". Color: brown. Range: Ore. (Page 194)

J.W.A.

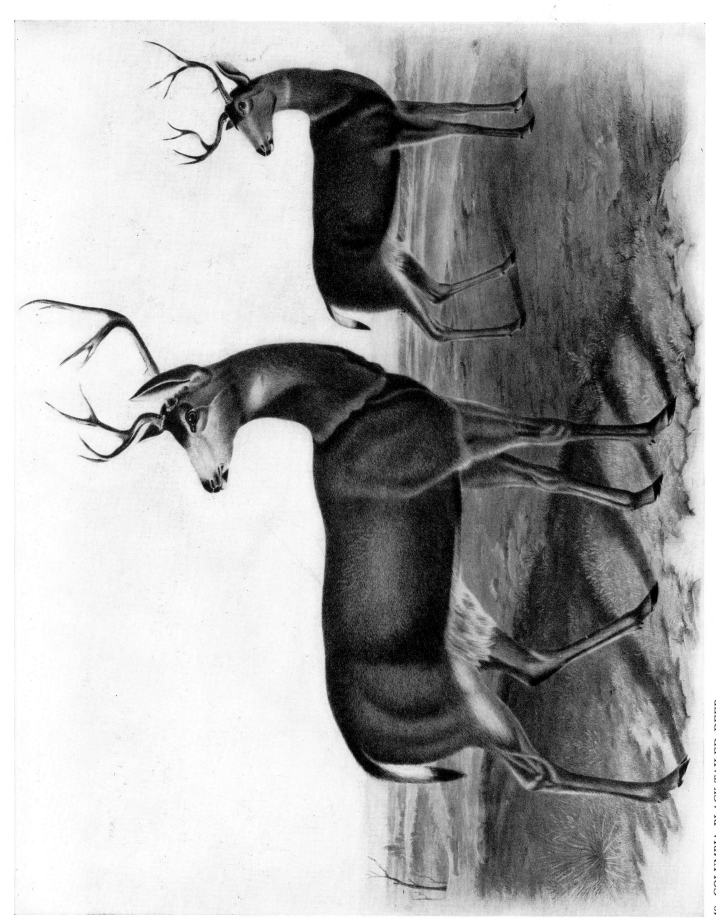

49. COLUMBIA BLACK-TAILED DEER.
Odocoileus columbianus. Males. Length: 5'4". Color: brown. Range: No. Calif. coastal mts. to B.C. (Page 105)

J.W.A.

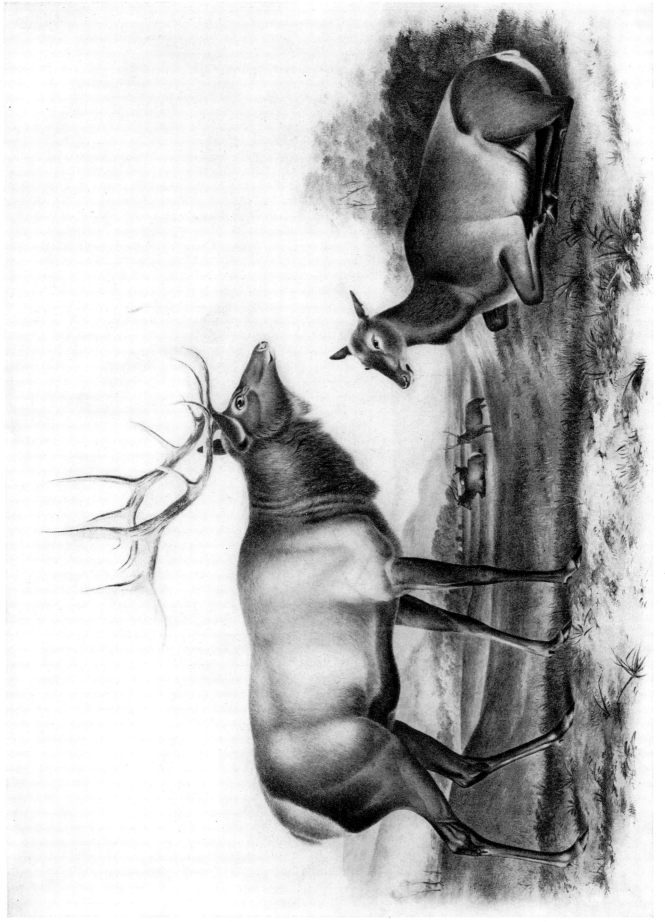

J.J.A.

50. AMERICAN ELK, WAPITI.
Cervus canadensis. Male and female. Length: 7'8¾". Color: brown. Range: western Canada, Mont., Wyo., Colo., and Pacific coast. (Page 195)

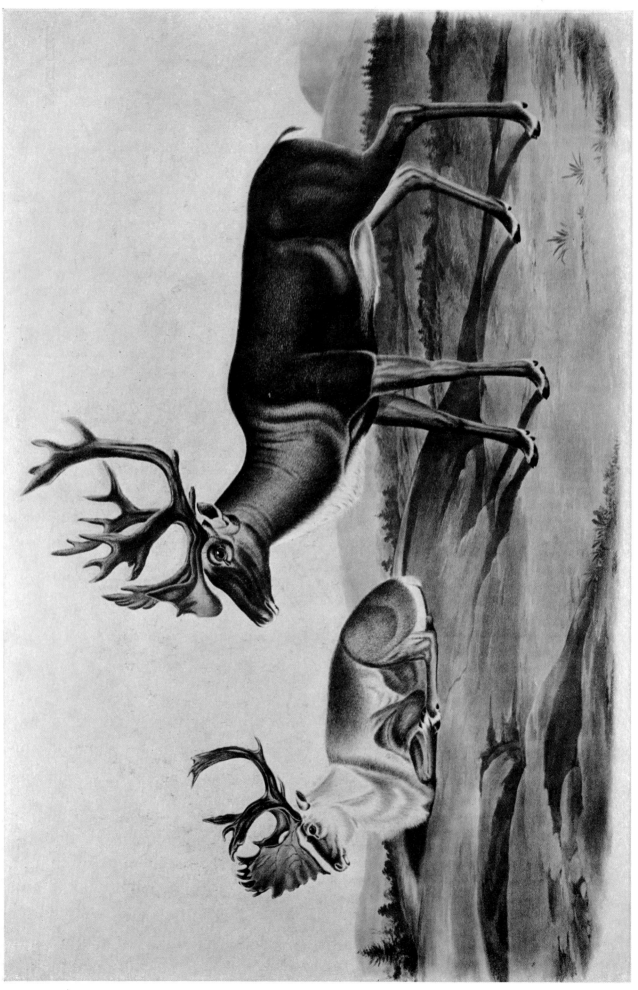

51. BARREN GROUND CARIBOU.
Rangifer arcticus. Males. Length: 6'. Color: brown; shown in summer and winter pelage. Range: Arctic Barren Ground region. (Page 196)

J.W.A.

122

52. MOOSE.　　　　　　*Alces americana.* Old male and young. Length: 6'11". Color: dark brown. Range: Canada and northern U.S. from Me. to Rockies. (Page 196)

J.W.A.

53. PRONG-HORNED ANTELOPE. *Antilocapra americana.* Male and female. Length: 4'2". Color: brown. Range: Rockies strip. (Page 196)

124

J.W.A.

54. ROCKY MOUNTAIN BIGHORN.
Ovis canadensis. Male and female. Length: 6'. Color: light grayish brown. Range: N.M. north to Alberta in mountainous regions. (Page 196)

55. ROCKY MOUNTAIN GOAT. *Oreamnos americanus.* Male and female. Length: 34". Color: white. Range: Alaska to Idaho. (Page 197)

J.W.A.

56. MUSK OX.

Ovibos moschatus. Males. Length: 5½'. Color: brown. Range: Arctic America from Mackenzie river and north of 60°, east to Melville Bay. (Page 197)

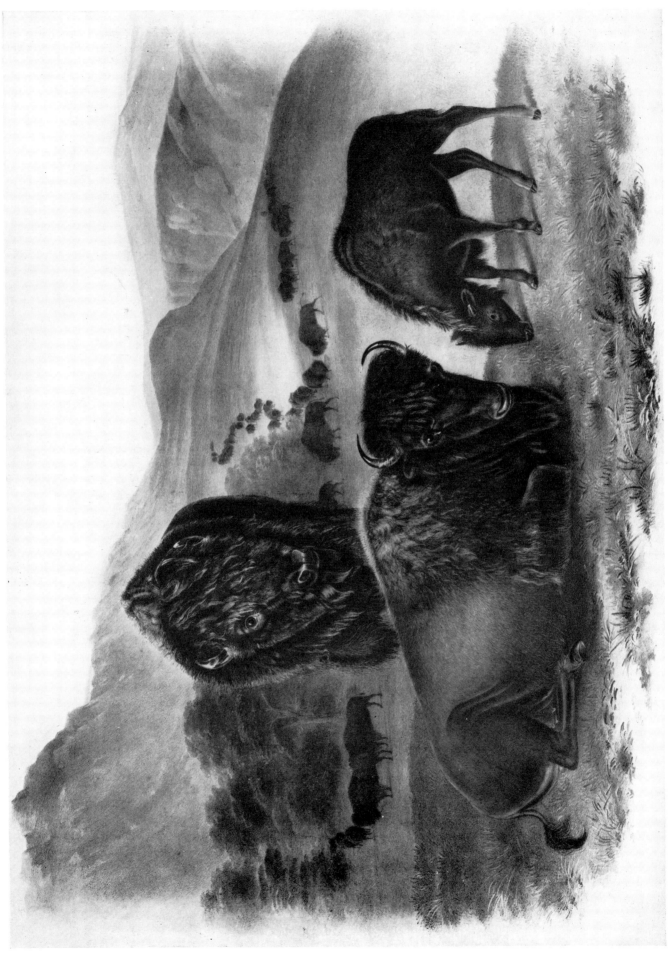

I.J.A.

57. AMERICAN BISON, BUFFALO. Length: 10'. Color: brownish black. Range: extinct in wild state; seen on reservations and in zoos only. (Page 197)
Bison bison. Female, male, and young.

58. AMERICAN BISON, BUFFALO.
Bison bison. Male. Length: 10′. Color: brownish black. Range: extinct in wild state; in zoos and reservations only. (Page 197)

J.J.A.

59. AMERICAN HARE, VARYING HARE, SNOWSHOE HARE, WHITE HARE, WHITE "RABBIT." *I.J.A.*
Lepus americanus americanus. Winter pelage. Length: 19¼". Color (*winter*): white, sometimes tinged with summer hue; ears black-edged. Range: eastern half of Canada, west to Saskatchewan, south to Mich. and Wyo. (Page 198)

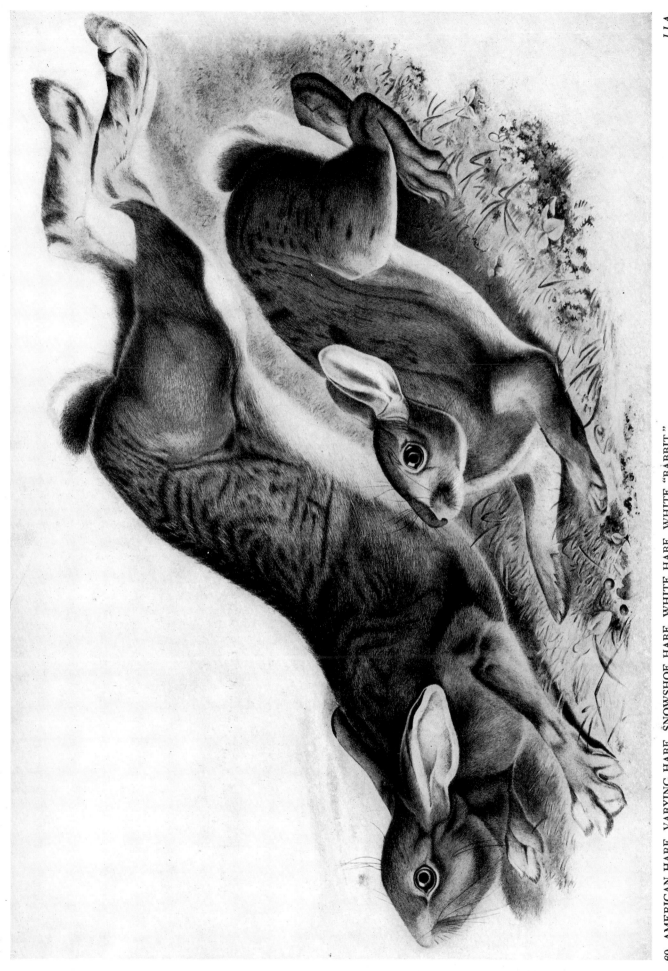

60. AMERICAN HARE, VARYING HARE, SNOWSHOE HARE, WHITE HARE, WHITE "RABBIT." *J.J.A.*
Lepus americanus americanus. Old male and young female. Summer pelage. Length: 19¼". Color (*summer*): reddish brown, black-tipped, April to Nov. Range: eastern half of Canada, west to Saskatchewan, south to Mich. and Wyo. (Page 198)

J.J.A.

61. PIKA, LITTLE CHIEF HARE, ROCK RABBIT, TAILLESS HARE, WHISTLING HARE, CONY.
Ochotona princeps. Males. Length: 6½″. Color: brown, banded with brownish black. Range: B.C. Rockies to Mackenzie river. (Page 198)

62. ARCTIC HARE. *Lepus arcticus.* Male. Summer pelage. Length: 26″. Color: white (winter); grayish brown (summer). Range: Baffin Land, Hudson Bay, Labrador. (Page 198)

J.J.A.

33. CALIFORNIA BRUSH RABBIT. *Sylvilagus bachmani*. Males. Length: 10″. Color: black-tipped brown. Range: Calif. (Page 198)

34. SWAMP RABBIT. *Sylvilagus aquaticus*. Male. Length: 20″. Color: brownish black with red-browns (winter); light brownish yellow (summer). Range: Ga. to Texas, north to Okla. and Ill. (Page 198)

65. MARSH RABBIT, CAROLINA SWAMP RABBIT.
Sylvilagus palustris. Male and female. Length: 13″. Color: yellowish brown mixed with black. Range: N.C. to Fla. (Page 199)

J.J.A.

134

J.W.A.

66. CALIFORNIA BLACK-TAILED JACK "RABBIT."
Lepus californicus. Length: 22″. Color: black and reddish brown. Range: Calif. desert plains. (Page 199)

135

67. WHITE-TAILED JACK "RABBIT," PRAIRIE HARE.   *J.J.A.*
Lepus townsendii. Male and female. Length: 21½". Color: gray, cream-tinged. Range: Great Basin to Wash., Rockies, Ore., Calif., north to B.C., east to Idaho, Wyo., Utah, and Colo. (Page 199)

68. TEXAS JACK "RABBIT." *Lepus californicus texianus.* Male. Length: 1'9". Color: brown. Range: Colo., Ariz., N.M., Texas. (Page 199)

J.W.A.

69. TEXAS JACK "RABBIT." *Lepus californicus texianus.* Male. Length: 20". Color: brown. Range: Colo., Ariz, N.M., Texas. (Page 199)

J.J.A.

70. COTTONTAIL, GRAY RABBIT.   *J.J.A.*
Sylvilagus floridanus. Old male, female, and young. Length: 15″. Color: black-tipped yellowish brown with gray tinge. Range: Fla. to N.C. to La.; subspecies throughout U.S. (Page 200) See also color plate on page 49.

71. WASHINGTON ROCKY MOUNTAIN COTTONTAIL RABBIT.
Sylvilagus nuttallii. Males. Length: 6¼″. Color: grayish black with brownish white. Range: Wash. Rockies. (Page 200)

J.W.A.

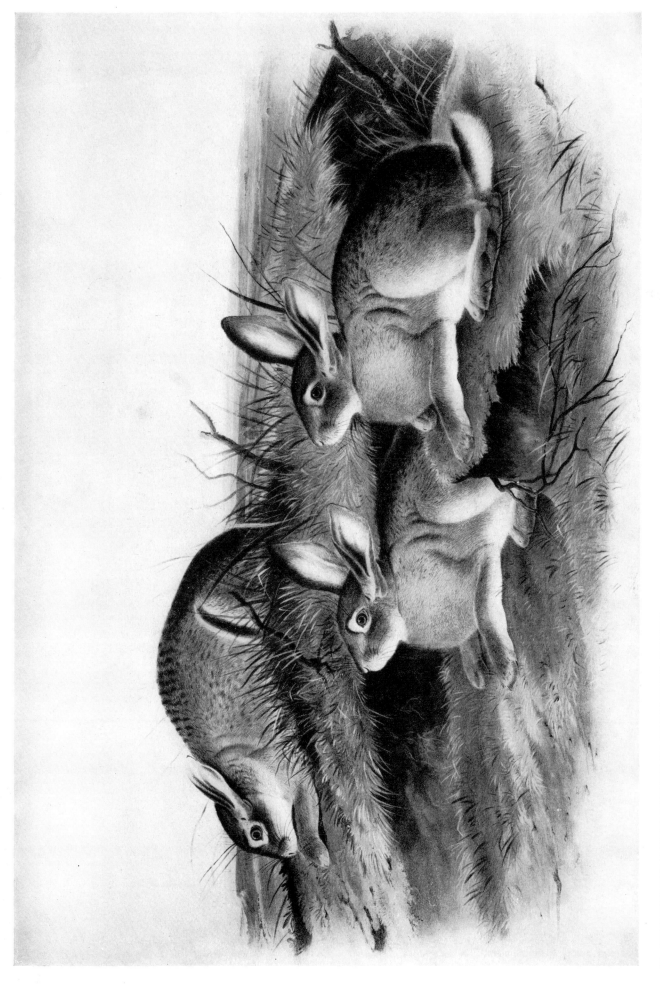

72. WASHINGTON ROCKY MOUNTAIN COTTONTAIL RABBIT. *J.J.A.*
Sylvilagus nuttallii. Males and female. Length: 12″. Color: grayish black with brownish white. Range: Wash. Rockies. (Page 200)

141

J.W.A.

73. GRAY SQUIRREL.

Male. Length: 12″. Named *Sciurus nigrescens* in *Quadrupeds,* this specimen is probably a melanistic or abnormally dark example of "one of the more common, perhaps Gray Squirrels," in the opinion of T. Donald Carter of the American Museum of Natural History. (Page 200)

Sciurus carolinensis carolinensis. Male and female. Length: 9½". Color: grayish and yellowish brown tipped with black; undersurface white. Range: N.Y. to Fla., west to Ind., Mo., and Okla. (Page 200)

74. EASTERN GRAY SQUIRREL, CAROLINA GRAY SQUIRREL.

J.J.A.

Sciurus carolinensis. Male and female. Length: 13″. Color: varies greatly, from light gray to almost black. Range: N.Y. to Fla., west to Ind., Mo., and Okla. (Page 200)

75. EASTERN GRAY SQUIRREL.

J.J.A.

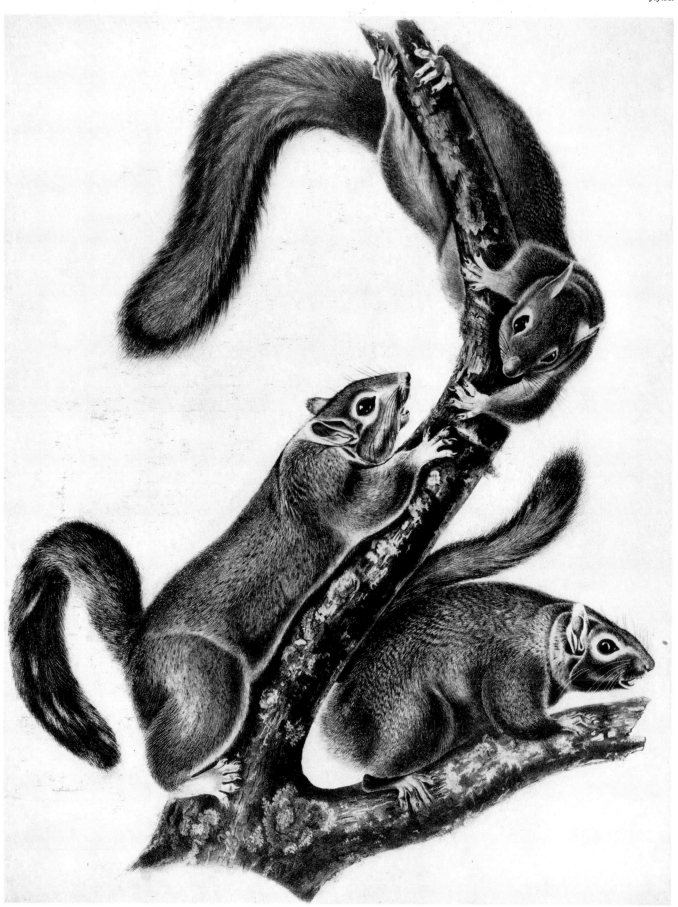

144

76. NORTHERN GRAY SQUIRREL.

Sciurus carolinensis leucotis. Male, female, and young. Length: 12″. Color: varies, gray or black as in Fig. 77. Range: N.E. states and Canada, from Ill., Ind., and Pa. north to 46° N. lat. and west to Minn. and Iowa. (Page 200)

145

J.J.A.

77. NORTHERN GRAY SQUIRREL.

Sciurus carolinensis leucotis. Male and female. Length: 13″. Color: This black specimen is a color variety of the species. Range: N.E. states and Canada, from Ill., Ind., and Pa. north to 46° N. lat. and west to Minn. and Iowa. (Page 200)

146

Sciurus griseus. Length: 11½″. Color: brownish gray. Range: pine and oak forests of Transition (and Upper Austral Zone) from Wash. to Ore. and Calif.; Mexico. (Page 201)

78. WESTERN GRAY SQUIRREL, CALIFORNIA GRAY SQUIRREL, COLUMBIA GRAY SQUIRREL.

J.J.A.

J.J.A.

Sciurus niger. Length: 14¾". Color: varies, black, gray, or brown. Range: Fla. and S.E. states. (Page 201)

79. FOX SQUIRREL.

148

80. WESTERN FOX SQUIRREL.
Sciurus niger rufiventer. Males. Length: 12″. Color: iron gray with cinnamon cast, black-tipped. Range: Mississippi valley, from La. to Wis. (Page 201)

J.J.A.

Sciurus niger rufiventer. Length: 13″. Color: black-tipped reddish brown. Range: most of Mississippi valley from La. to Wis. (Page 201)

81. WESTERN FOX SQUIRREL, YELLOW-BELLIED FOX SQUIRREL.

J.J.A.

82. WESTERN FOX SQUIRREL or TEXAS FOX SQUIRREL.

Male and female. Length: 10½". Color: black-tipped reddish brown. If this is the Texas Fox Squirrel (*Sciurus niger texianus*) the range is: coastal La. and Mississippi. If it is the Western Fox Squirrel (*Sciurus niger rufiventer*), the range is most of Mississippi valley from La. to Wis.. (Page 201)

151

83. FREMONT'S CHICKAREE, PINE SQUIRREL (*left*). *Tamiasciurus fremonti*. Length: 7″. Color: gray. Range: Colo. Rockies; Utah in Uinta mts. BLACK FOX SQUIRREL (*right*). *Sciurus niger niger*. Length: 10″. Color: black. Range: Fla. and southeastern states. (Page 202)

J.W.A.

152

J.W.A.

84. COLLIE'S SQUIRREL.

Sciurus colliaei. Males. Length: 10″. Color: grizzled gray-brown. Range: Mexico. (Page 202)

Tamiasciurus hudsonicus vancouverensis. Length: 7″. Color: chestnut-brown-tipped gray; white undersurface. Range: Sitka, south to Vancouver Island. (Page 202)

85. VANCOUVER RED SQUIRREL.

J.J.A.

86. RICHARDSON'S RED SQUIRREL.

Tamiasciurus hudsonicus richardsoni. Male and female. Length: 6¼". Color: rusty brown and black; light undersurface. Range: Yellowstone Park, West, Northwest. (Page 202) See color detail, page 61.

155

J.J.A

87. REDWOOD CHICKAREE, RED SQUIRREL.

Tamiasciurus douglasii mollipilosus. Length: 8″. Color: dark brown, black-tinged; tail twice black-annulated; light belly. Range: Calif. an
Ore. (Page 202)

Tamiasciurus hudsonicus. Male and female. Length: 8″. Color: deep reddish brown; undersurface light. Range: boreal North America, Labrador to Rockies and Alaska. (Page 202)

88. EASTERN RED SQUIRREL, CHICKAREE.

J.J.A.

Tamiasciurus douglasii. Length: 11⅞". Color: blackish brown, with gray and light brown; brownish black and light-brown tail. Range: Wash. and Ore. (Page 202)

89. DOUGLAS'S CHICKAREE.

J.J.A.

90. DOUGLAS'S CHICKAREE.

Tamiasciurus douglasii. Male and female. Length: 8¼″. Color: rusty dark-brown; undersurface lighter. Range: Wash. and Ore. coasts from Cape Blanco to Puget Sound. (Page 203)

Sciurus aureogaster. Male, female, and young. Length: 8½″. Color: light gray; undersurface reddish. Range: Mexico. (Page 203)

91. RED-BELLIED SQUIRREL.

J.J.A.

92. EASTERN FLYING SQUIRREL.

Glaucomys volans. Males, females, and young. Length: 5¼″. Color: dark slate gray, with yellowish brown tinge. Range: N.Y., N.H. to Fla., west to Plains. (Page 203)

161

93. OLYMPIC FLYING SQUIRREL.

Glaucomys sabrinus olympicus. Male and female. Length: 6½". Color: black-tipped, yellowish-brown-tipped dark brown; light undersurface.
Range: Olympic mts. (Page 203)

94. NORTHERN FLYING SQUIRREL (*left*). *Glaucomys sabrinus sabrinus.* Length: 8″. Color: reddish brown. Range: boreal North America to N.Y. and N.H. RICHARDSON'S FLYING SQUIRREL (*right*). *Glaucomys sabrinus alpinus.* Length: 8½″. Color: brown. Range: Canadian Rockies. (Page 203)

J.W.A.

95. EASTERN CHIPMUNK.

Tamias striatus striatus. Male, female, and young. Length: 6″. Color: yellowish and chestnut brown with stripes; white undersurface. Range: North, South, Midwest. (Page 203)

J.J.A.

96. SAY'S CHIPMUNK. *Eutamias quadrivittatus.* Male, female, and young. Length: 4⅜". Color: browns with five dark and four pale lines. Range: Colo., Rockies, N.M., Ariz. (Page 204)

97. THIRTEEN-STRIPED GROUND SQUIRREL. *Citellus tridecemlineatus.* Male and female. Length: 6¾". Color: striped brown and yellowish white. Range: central North America in prairie region. (Page 204)

J.J.A.

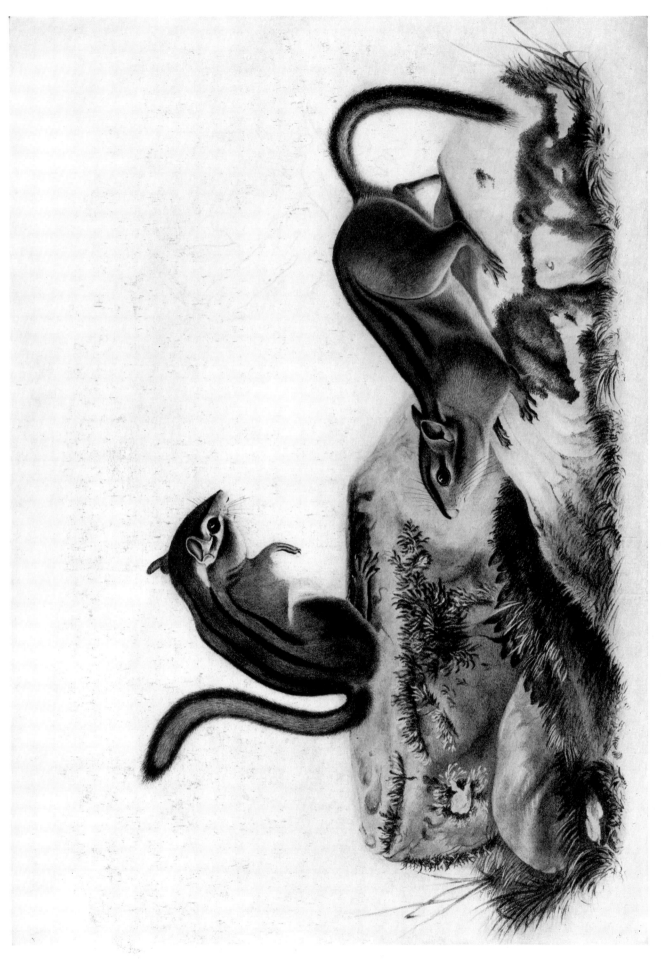

J.J.A.

98. TOWNSEND'S CHIPMUNK.
Eutamias townsendii. Length: 6″. Color: generally brown, black-striped; gray belly. Range: Neb. to Columbia river plains, Wyo., Utah, Mont., Idaho, Ore. (Page 204)

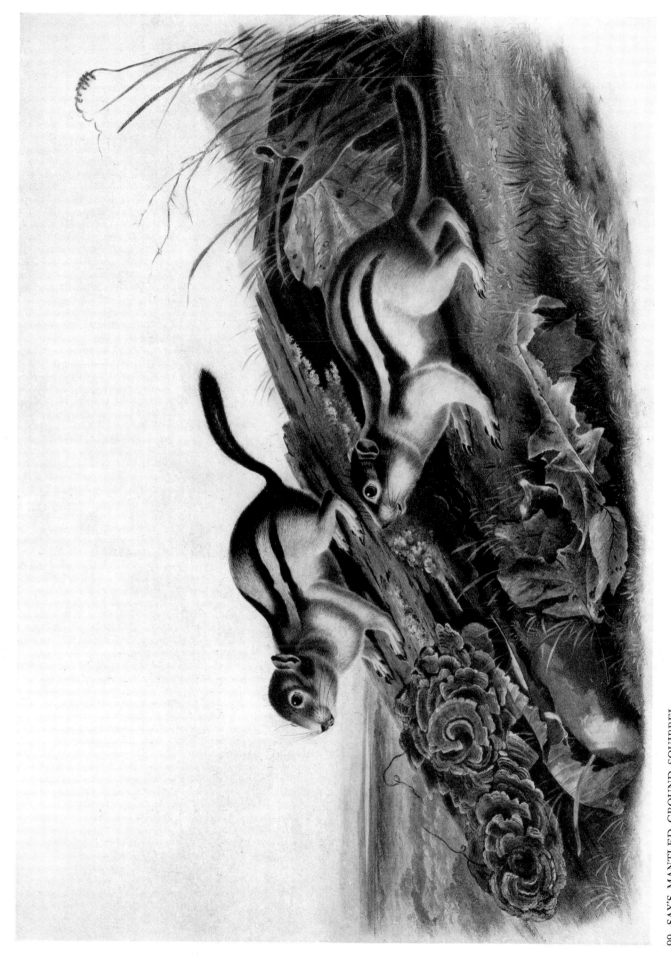

J.W.A.

99. SAY'S MANTLED GROUND SQUIRREL.
Citellus lateralis. Length: 8". Color: hoary brownish gray, striped. Range: Wyo., Colo., Utah, Ariz., N.M., Calif. (Page 204)

100. RICHARDSON'S GROUND SQUIRREL. *Citellus richardsonii.* Length: 9¼". Color: yellowish brown. Range: Saskatchewan, 55° N. lat., south to S.D. and Mont. (Page 205)

101. HUDSON BAY GROUND SQUIRREL. *Citellus parryii.* Male. Length: 11¼". Color: yellowish white with black tips; black annulations; rusty undersurface. Range: Hudson Bay; related species west to Columbia river. (Page 205)

168

102. MEXICAN GROUND SQUIRREL.

Citellus mexicanus. Male. Length: 10″.
Color: brown. Range: Mexico. (Page 205)

J.W.A.

103. MEXICAN GROUND SQUIRREL.

Citellus mexicanus. Young. [Fig. 102
shows adult male.] (Page 205)

J.W.A.

104. MEXICAN ROCK SQUIRREL.

Citellus variegatus. Male. Length: 1′1″.
Color: annulated, grizzled blackish gray.
Range: Mexico. (Page 205)

J.W.A.

J.J.A.

105. RING-TAILED GROUND SQUIRREL. *Citellus annulatus.* Male. Length: 8″. Color: speckled dark-grayish brown. Range: Mexico. (Page 205)

106. DOUGLAS'S GROUND SQUIRREL. *Citellus beecheyi douglasii.* Length: 13¾″. Color: hoary dark-brown. Range: Colo., Wash., and Calif. (Page 205)

J.J.A.

170

107 (*above*). FRANKLIN'S SPERMOPHILE.

Citellus franklinii. Male and female. Length: 9¾". Color: black-lined grayish brown; speckled appearance. Range: Ind. to Mo., Kans. and Neb.; north to Saskatchewan. (Page 205)

108. BLACK-TAILED PRAIRIE DOG.

Cynomys ludovicianus. Male, female, and young. Length: 13". Color: brown. Range: Texas, Kans., to eastern base of Rockies. (Page 205)

109. WHITE-TAILED PRAIRIE DOG.

Cynomys leucurus. Males. Length: 1'4". Color: brown. Range: Wyo. and Colo. In 1898 Dr. J. A. Allen proposed reviving Audubon's name for this species: *Arctomys lewisii.* In 1915 Mr. Oldfield Thomas studied the actual specimen and declared it a species of *Marmota.* (Page 206)

110. YELLOW-BELLIED MARMOT.
Marmota flaviventris flaviventris. Male. Length: 16″. Color: black-tipped yellowish brown, yellow belly. Range: Mt. Hood, Wash. (Page 206)

111. HOARY MARMOT, GRAY MARMOT, WHISTLING MARMOT.
Marmota caligata. Males. Length: 1'7". Color: hoary brown. Range: Columbia river to Barren Ground, east to Hudson Bay. (Page 206)

112. EASTERN WOODCHUCK.
Marmota monax. Female and young. Length: 18¾″ (male). Color: varies, black to brown, reddish, gray, etc. Range: N.Y. to Dakotas; Tenn., Ky., Va., and northward. (Page 206)

J.J.A.

113. BEAVER.

Castor canadensis. Length: 23″. Color: chestnut brown. Range: 40° N. lat. north to Labrador, Hudson Bay; western Arctic Circle west to Cascade mountains. (Page 206)

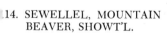

114. SEWELLEL, MOUNTAIN
BEAVER, SHOWT'L.

Aplodontia rufa. Male. Length:
4″. Color: black-tipped brown.
Range: Ore. and Wash. (Page
206)

175

115. PINE VOLE.

Pitymys pinetorum pinetorum. Male and female. Length: 4¼". Color: brown with gray hue. Range: Ga., N.C., S.C. (Page 207)

J.J.A.

116. RICHARDSON'S VOLE (*left*). *Microtus richardsoni richardsoni.* Length: 7". Color: blackish gray. Range: Alberta, Canada. **DRUMMOND'S VOLE** (*right*). *Microtus drummondii.* Length: 4". Color: brown. Range: Hudson Bay; Alaska; U.S. border to Ft. Anderson, Mackenzie. (Page 207)

J.W.A.

117. YELLOW-CHEEKED VOLE.

Microtus xanthognathus. Adult and young. Length: 8". Color: mixed dark brown and black. Range: N.W. Canada, and Alaska to Arctic coast. (Page 207)

J.W.A.

119 (*below*). RICHARDSON'S
LEMMING.

Synaptomys borealis. Male and
female. Length: 4⅜″. Color: dark
reddish brown. Range: Canada.
(Page 207)

J.W.A.

118 (*above*). TOWNSEND'S GROUND
SQUIRREL (*left*). *Citellus townsendii.*
Length: 8½″. Color: blackish gray. Range:
Neb. west to Colo. river plains; from Wyo.
and Utah to Mont., Idaho, and Ore. TEXAS
COTTON RAT (*right*). *Sigmodon hispidus
texianus.* Length: 4½″. Color: brown.
Range: Texas north to Kans. OREGON
VOLE (*center*). *Microtus oregoni oregoni.*
Length: 3″. Color: brown. Range: Pacific
coast. (Page 207)

J.W.A.   J.W.A.

120 (*below*). AMERICAN LEMMING (*left
and center*). *Lemmus trimucronatus.* Length: 5″.
Color: brown. Range: Arctic America. TAWNY
LEMMING (*right*). *Lemmus helvolus.*
Length: 4⅜″. Color: brown. Range: Arctic re-
gions. (Pages 207, 208)

J.W.A.

121 (*left*). COLLARED LEMMING.

Dicrostonyx hudsonius. Length: 5¼″. Color: *left*, white (winter); *right*, brown (summer). Range: Labrador. (Page 208)

122 (*below*). MEADOW JUMPING MOUSE.

Zapus hudsonius. Male and female. Length: 2⅜″. Color: varies, yellowish brown or darker; light undersurface. Range: Hudson Bay to N.J., N.C. mts. to Iowa and Mo., north to Alaska. (Page 208)

J.J.A.

123 (*below*). HOUSE MOUSE.

Mus musculus. Male, female, and young. Length: 3¼″. Color: gray. Range: wide. (Page 208)

J.W.A.

124 (*above*). EASTERN WHITE-FOOTED MOUSE, DEER MOUSE, WOOD MOUSE.

Peromyscus leucopus. Male, female, and young. Length: 2¼″. Color: brownish yellow (winter); light mouse color (summer); white undersurface. Range: N.E. Canada from Labrador, Hudson Bay, south to N.E. states. (Page 208)

126 (*below*). COMMON MEADOW MOUSE.

Microtus pennsylvanicus. Length: 5″. Color: gray. Range: eastern states, west to Dakotas and Neb. (Page 209)

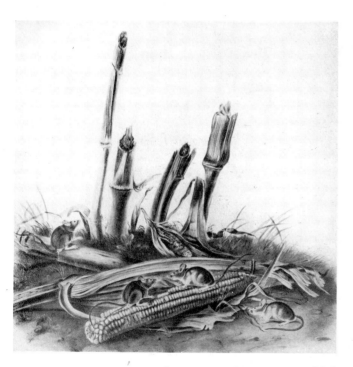

125 (*above*). HARVEST MOUSE.

Reithrodontomys humulis. Length: 2¾″. Color: gray with fawn tones. Range: coastal S.C., Ga., south to Fla. (Page 209)

179

127. SOUTHERN GOLDEN MOUSE.

Peromyscus nuttalli aureolus. Male and female. Length: 4⅛″. Color: bright orange; buff belly. Range: N.C. to Fla., west to Texas and Okla. (Lower Austral region.) (Page 209)

J.W.A.

J.W.A.

128. AUDUBON GRASSHOPPER MOUSE.

Onychomys leucogaster missouriensis. Females. Length: 4½″. Color: fawn and white. Range: N.D., Mont., Wyo., Canada. (Page 209)

129. TOWNSEND'S MEADOW MOUSE (*left*). *Microtus townsendii.* Length: 6″. Color: gray. Range: Puget Sound region to Calif. MEADOW VOLE (*center*). *Microtus pennsylvanicus.* Length: 5½″. Color: grayish black. Range: Most of U.S. SWAMP RICE RAT, RICE MEADOW MOUSE (*right*). *Oryzomys palustris.* Length: 5⅛″. Color: dark grayish brown. Range: North America from N.J. to Fla. and Gulf states. (Page 209)

J.W.A.

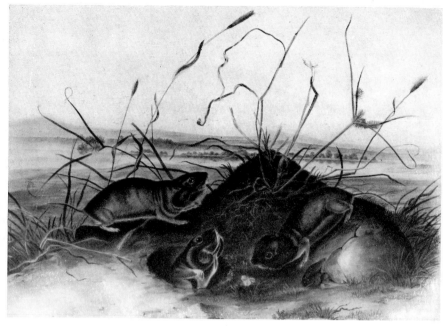

J.W.A.

130. DOUGLAS'S POCKET GOPHER.

Thomomys douglasii. Males. Length: 6¼″. Color: brown. Range: along Columbia river near Vancouver; Wash. (Page 209)

131. SASKATCHEWAN POCKET GOPHER.

Thomomys talpoides. Males. Length: 7¼″. Color: grayish black. Range: Saskatchewan plains, Alberta, south to Mont. (Page 209)

J.W.A.

J.W.A.

132. CAMAS POCKET GOPHER.

Thomomys bulbivorus. Male, female, and young. Length: 7⅜″. Color: yellowish pale gray. Range: Ore. (Page 209)

133. SHAW POCKET GOPHER.

Geomys bursarius. Males, female, and young. Length: 9¾". Color: gray (darker in winter). Range: Upper Mississippi valley from Kans., Mo., Ill., the Dakotas, and Neb. east to Lake Michigan. (Page 210)

J.J.A.

J.J.A.

134. EASTERN MUSKRAT.

Ondatra zibethica. Old and young. Length: 15". Color: dark brown with reddish tints. Range: S.E. Canada; N.E. and E.C. states. (Page 210)

135. BUSHY-TAILED WOOD RAT.

Neotoma cinerea drummondii. Length: 9". Color: dark brown mixed with yellowish brown, black-tipped (winter); gray (summer). Range: Rockies; B.C. to Ariz., Nev., Calif. (Page 210)

J.J.A.

136. KANGAROO RAT.

Dipodomys agilis. Males. Length: 5″.
Color: brown above; white below; tail
brown and white. Range: Calif. (Page 210)

J.W.A.

137. COTTON RAT.

Sigmodon hispidus. Length: 6″. Color:
reddish brown with gray tinge; whitish
undersurface. Range: eastern states; Carolinas to Fla. (Page 210)

J.J.A.

138. BLACK RAT.

Rattus rattus rattus. Old and young.
Length: 8″. Color: bluish black with gray
lights. Range: mostly South and Southwest. (Page 210)

J.J.A.

139. EASTERN WOOD RAT.

Neotoma floridana. Male, female, and young.
Length: 8″. Color: lead tinged with yellow
and black; undersurface creamy white. Range:
South Atlantic and Gulf coast and lower Mississippi valley. (Page 211)

140. BROWN RAT, NORWAY RAT.

Rattus norvegicus. Male and female with young.
Length: 10″. Color: black-tinged brown. Range:
wide. (Page 211)

J.J.A.

J.J.A.

141. CANADA PORCUPINE.

Erethizon dorsatum. Male. Length: 29″. Color: black or brownish black. Range: eastern North America (40° N.lat.) to Hudson Bay, to Arctic Circle and Alaska. (Page 211)

185

142 (*above left*). COMMON STAR-NOSED MOLE. *Condylura cristata*. Length: 5″. Color: black. Range: eastern North America. 143 (*above right*). BREWER'S MOLE. *Parascalops breweri*. Length: 5¾″. Color: black. Range: N.C., W.Va., Ohio, Pa., N.J., and N.Y. 144. (*below left*) OREGON MOLE. *Scapanus townsendii*. Length: 8½″. Color: dark brown and black. Range: Ore., Wash., and Calif. 145 (*below right*). FLORIDA POCKET GOPHER (*left*). *Geomys floridanus*. Length: 8¾″. Color: yellowish black. Range: Fla., St. Augustine region. SHORT-TAILED SHREW (*center*). *Blarina brevicauda*. Length: 4½″. Color: rusty yellow gray. Range: eastern U.S. CAROLINA SHREW (*right*). *Sorex longirostris*. Length: 1⅞″. Color: chestnut. Range: N.C., S.C., and Ga., west to Ill., north to B.C. COMMON MOLE, PRAIRIE MOLE (*right foreground*). *Scalopus aquaticus*. Length: 7″. Color: silvery. Range: eastern North America. (Page 212)

186

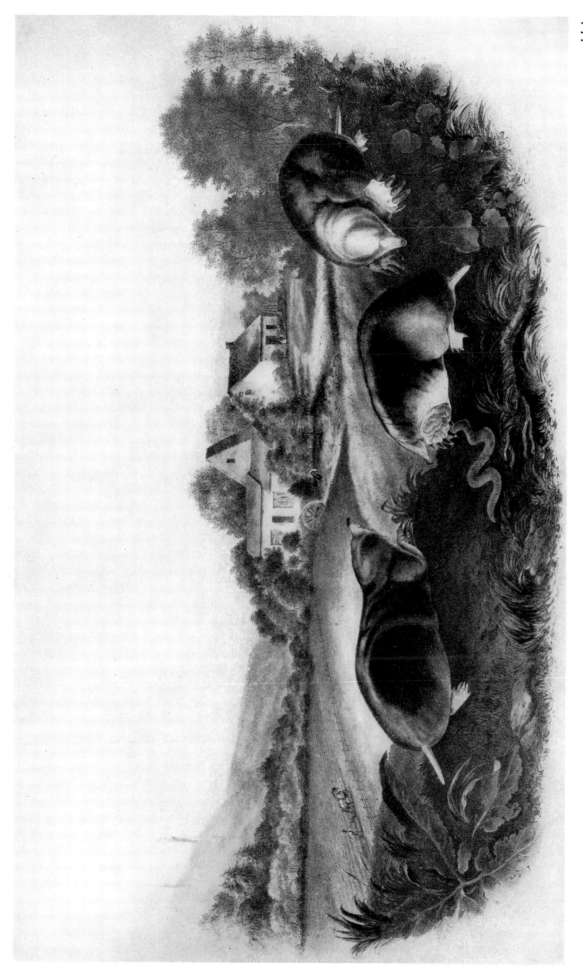

J.J.A.

146. COMMON MOLE.

Scalopus aquaticus. Male and female. Length: 5½″. Color: gray with browns; often nearly black. Range: eastern states south to Fla., west to Mississippi. (Page 212)

J.J.A.

147 (*above*). CAROLINA
SHORT-TAILED SHREW.

Blarina brevicauda carolinensis. Male and
females. Length: 3". Color: black. Range:
mouth of Chesapeake Bay to Ark. (Page
213)

148 (*right*). WATER SHREW.

Neosorex palustris. Males. Length: 3".
Color: hoary black above; ash-color be-
low. Range: Minn. to east base of Rockies.
(Page 213)

149 (*below*). LITTLE SHORT-TAILED
SHREW.

Cryptotis parva. Length: 2⅞". Color:
brown-tipped gray. Range: Texas to Neb.,
east to Atlantic coast. (Page 213)

J.W.A.

(*opposite page*)

150. VIRGINIA OPOSSUM.

Didelphis virginiana. Female and
young male (7 mos. old).
Length: Female: 15½". Color:
black-tipped grayish white.
Range: N.Y. to Fla., west to Miss.
and Tex. (Page 213)

J.J.A.

150. VIRGINIA OPOSSUM. (Description on opposite page.)

The following plates, not to be found in the Imperial folio edition of *The Viviparous Quadrupeds of North America*, were added to the original miniature (Royal octavo) edition as Plates CLI-CLV. A sixth plate, CXXIV, "Mountain Brook Mink" [American Mink], was published to fill the space left vacant by the merging of folio Plates CIX and CXXIV to make octavo Plate CIX.

J.W.A.

151. BLACK FOX SQUIRREL, SOUTHERN FOX SQUIRREL (*left*). *Sciurus niger niger*. Male. Length: 10″. Color: black. Range: S.E. states and Fla. RED-BELLIED SQUIRREL (*right*). *Sciurus aureogaster*. Male. Length: 11″. Color: brownish gray; reddish undersurface. Range: Mexico. (Page 214)

152. HARRIS'S ANTELOPE GROUND SQUIRREL *(left)*. *Ammospermophilus harrisii harrisii.* Length: 5¾". Color: speckled yellowish brown. Range: Utah, Nev., Calif., N.M. CALIFORNIA VOLE *(right)*. *Microtus californicus.* Length: 5½". Color: grayish black. Range: Calif. to Ore. (Page 216)

153. WESTERN, or CALIFORNIA, GRAY SQUIRREL *(left)*. *Sciurus griseus.* Length: 12". Color: gray. Range: northern Calif., Ore., Wash. COLONEL ABERT'S SQUIRREL *(right)*. *Sciurus aberti.* Length: 13". Color: gray above; white below. Range: Ariz. and N.M. (Page 214)

154. LONG-TAILED RED FOX.

Vulpes macroura. Length: 2'8".
Color: grayish brown. Range: mts.
of Colo., Utah, and Wyo. (Page
214)

155. CRAB-EATING RACCOON.

Procyon cancrivorus. Length: 22".
Color: yellowish brown. Range:
Calif. and Mexico. (Page 214)

J.W.A.

156. AMERICAN MINK.

Mustela vison vison. Male. Length:
11". Color: blackish brown. Range:
eastern Canada to Rockies south
through Central America. (Page
214)

J.W.A.

(Continued from page 77)

of Mr. McFadden, who kept a house of entertainment for man and beast, which, by this time, was greatly needed by the travellers."

—Quads. Vol. II, p. 19.

Fig. 42. HOODED SKUNK *(page 113)*

"The specimen figured by John Woodhouse Audubon was obtained near San Antonio, and he describes it as common in western Texas. Its superb tail is now and then used by the country folks as a plume or feather for their hats. J. W. Audubon, in his Journal, remarks: 'We were much amused at the disposition of the privates in the corps of Rangers to put on extra finery when opportunity offered. At one time a party returned from a chase after Indians whom they had overtaken and routed, and several of them had whole Turkey cocks' tails stuck on the side of their hats, and long pendant trains of feathers hanging behind their backs, which they had taken from the Wakoe Indian braves. One young fellow had a superb head-dress and suit to match which he had scared out of an Indian, and to complete the triumphal decoration of his handsome person, he had painted his face all the colors of the rainbow.'"

—Quads. Vol. III, pp. 13, 16.

Fig. 43. TEXAS NINE-BANDED ARMADILLO *(page 114)*

"This singular production of nature resembles a small pig saddled with the shell of a turtle. Its covering is something between turtle-shell or horn and very hard sole leather. The Armadillo is not a 'fighting character,' but on the contrary is more peaceable than the Opossum.

"A friend of ours who formerly resided in South America had a pet Armadillo in his bed-chamber. It generally remained quiet by day, but in the dark hours was active and playful. One night it began dragging the chairs and some boxes about, and continued so busily engaged at this occupation that our friend could not sleep. He arose, struck a light, and to his surprise found boxes he had supposed much too heavy for such an animal to stir had been placed together to form a sort of den or hiding place in a corner, in which the animal retreated with great apparent satisfaction. It could only be drawn out after a hard struggle.

"When the Armadillo has a chance of escape by digging into the ground, it is no sluggard. On being much alarmed it rolls itself up but does not attempt to flee. In Nicaragua the people of the ranchos keep it to free their houses from ants, which it can follow by smell, putting out its tongue and scraping the ants into its mouth. When a line of ants (which may extend some distance into the woods) are busily carrying provision to their general storehouse, they scatter at the instant the Armadillo begins digging towards it, evidently having some communication from headquarters equivalent to *sauve qui peut*. Their gait is like that of a tortoise, and their nails are powerfully organized for digging. It is found in Guiana and Central America, and is common in Mexico and southern Texas.

"The Armadillo is generally much darker in color than the specimen we figured, which, having been a pet, was washed and clean when we drew it. In the woods they partake more or less of the color of the soil. Except for the domesticated ones, these animals live in burrows, under rocks, or in the roots of trees."

—Quads. Vol. III, pp. 221, 222, 223, 224.

Fig. 44. COLLARED PECCARY *(page 115)*

"Although they are usually found in the forests and prefer low and marshy grounds, like common hogs, Peccaries wander wherever they can find an abundance of food. They often enter the enclosures of the planters and commit great depredations on the products of their fields. When attacked by the Jaguar, the Puma, the Wolf, or the dog of the hunter, they form a circle, surrounding and protecting their young, repelling their opponents with their sharp teeth; and in this manner they sometimes rout the larger predatory animals, or severely wound the dogs and the hunters. When angry they gnash their teeth and raise their bristles, and their sharp shrill grunt can be heard at a distance.

"William P. Smith was sent to this country by our kind friend the Earl of Derby, to procure living animals to enrich his collection at Knowsley near Liverpool. We engaged him also to obtain for us any rare species he could meet with in Texas, where he went in 1841. He says:

" 'The Mexican hogs struck terror into the hearts

of the settlers, previous to the overflowing of the bottom lands in 1833. Oftentimes they pursued the planter whilst he was hunting or in search of wandering cattle. They frequently killed his dogs, or even forced him to ascend a tree for safety. They would snap their teeth, run about the tree, and then lie down at the foot of it to wait for their enemy to come down. He would wait until the hogs got tired or left him to go and feed. At this period from five to fifteen planters, and occasionally a larger number of hunters, used to hunt this animal in company, to diminish the ravagers of their corn-fields, as at times they would nearly destroy a farmer's crop. The two I send you are the only ones I have heard of since my arrival. We closed the entrance of their hole and cut a large opening up the tree, a few feet above them. From that vantage point we were enabled easily to drop a noose around their necks, which we tightened until we thought they were nearly suffocated. We drew them out, tied their legs and feet securely, bound their jaws, and left them lying on the ground for a time. We then put them across a horse. This is the usual mode of taking these animals alive, although some are caught in pits.'"

—*Quads. Vol. I, pp. 236–237, 238.*

Figs. 45 and 46. VIRGINIA DEER OR WHITE-TAILED DEER (pages 116, 117)

"Perhaps no wild animal inhabiting North America deserves to be regarded with more interest. The savory qualities of its flesh are well known. The skin is of the greatest service to the wild man and also useful to the dweller in towns. Dressed and smoked by the squaws until soft and pliable, it will not shrink with all the soaking to which it is exposed. For moccasins, leggings and hunting shirts it is the dress of many Indian tribes, and in the civilized world is used for breeches, gloves and gaiters. From the horns are made beautiful cutlery handles.

"The young fawns, when but a few days old, are often found in so sound a sleep in a covert of grass beneath a fallen tree-top that we have seen them taken up in arms before they became conscious that they were captives. Easily domesticated, they attach themselves to their keepers in a few hours. We have seen them reared by a cow, but a goat becomes

the best foster mother. We have found them troublesome pets. A pair that we had for several years were in the habit of leaping into our study through the open window, and when the sashes were down they still bounced through, carrying along with them the shattered glass. They licked and gnawed the covers of our books and created confusion among our papers. No shrub in the garden was sacred to them. They gnawed our carriage harness, and finally pounced upon our young ducks and chickens.

"The Deer is one of the most silent of animals. The fawn has a gentle bleat, but we have never heard the voice of the female beyond a murmur when calling her young. The buck utters a snort, and we have heard him emitting a shrill whistling sound at night not unlike the Alpine Chamois."

—*Quads. Vol. II, pp. 221–222, 226.*

Fig. 47. MULE DEER (page 118)

"We have figured a female in summer pelage, and have represented the animal in an exhausted state, wounded through the body, and about to drop down, while the hunter is seen approaching through tall grass.

"Through the aid of our hunters near Fort Union we obtained the Deer from which our figure, description, and measurements were made."

—*Quads. Vol. II, p. 209.*

Fig. 48. OREGON WHITE-TAILED DEER (page 119)

"We have given what we consider an excellent figure by J. W. Audubon, from the original specimen. In its general appearance this Deer resembles the European roebuck."

—*Quads. Vol. III, p. 80.*

From the Missouri River Journal, August 2, 1843:

"I have been examining the fawn of the Long-tailed Deer of this country, belonging to old Baptiste; the man feeds it regularly, and the fawn follows him everywhere. It will race backwards and forwards over the prairie back of the fort, for a mile or more, running at the very top of its speed; suddenly it will make for the gate, rush through and overwhelm Baptiste with caresses, as if it had actually lost him for some time. If Baptiste lies on the ground pretending to sleep, the fawn pushes with its nose, and licks his face as a dog would, till he wakens."

Fig. 49. COLUMBIA BLACK-TAILED DEER (page 120)

"This beautiful animal was first noticed by Lewis and Clark near the mouth of the Columbia river, but not until the discovery of gold in California did it become generally known to white men."
—*Quads. Vol. III, p. 28.*

Fig. 50. AMERICAN ELK OR WAPITI (page 121)

"On our plate we have represented a pair of Elks in the foreground of a prairie scene. Observe the splendid buck as he walks lightly, proudly, and gracefully along. It is the season of love: his head is raised above the willows bordering the large sandbar on the shores of the Missouri . . . his neck is arched . . . every vein is distended. He looks around and snuffs the morning air with dilated nostrils: he stamps the earth and utters a shrill cry somewhat like the noise of the loon. When he discovers a group of females he raises his head, inclines it backward, and giving another trumpet-like whistle, dashes off to meet them, making the willows and other small trees yield and crack as he rushes by. Finding a buck as large and brave as himself gallanting the fair objects of his pursuit, his eyes glow with rage and jealousy, his teeth are fiercely champed together making a loud harsh noise, and his hair stands erect. With the points of his immense horns lowered like the lance of a doughty knight, he leaps toward his rival. A desperate battle ensues, the combatants swaying backwards and forwards or in circles, writhing as they endeavor to throw their opponent off the ground. At length our valorous Elk triumphs. Should there be any young Elks present during such a combat they generally run off.

"The victorious buck leads the does to the sandbars or the willow-covered points along the stream. After a certain period, however, he leaves them to other bucks, and towards late February his antlers drop off, his body is emaciated, and he retires to some secluded spot, where he hopes no enemies will discover him, as he is no longer vigorous and bold, and would dread to encounter even a single wolf.

"Whilst ascending the Missouri in the steamer *Omega* we saw a fawn of this species one morning, running along the shore. It was covered with yellowish white spots, was nimble and active as a kitten, and quickly reached a place where it could ascend the bank. We soon saw another fawn. The boat having stopped to take on wood, an expert hunter climbed the bank and overtook the little animal. Having no rope with him, he took off his suspenders, and with these and his pocket handkerchief he managed to fasten the fawn around the neck. But the suspenders gave way and the fawn dropped into the stream and swam off.

"At Fort Pierre we were presented with a most splendid pair of superb male Elk horns, four feet six and a half inches long, and twenty-seven and a half inches broad between the points. This animal was one of the largest ever seen by Mr. Picot, who killed it in November, 1832.

"The pair from which the figures on the plate were taken we purchased at Philadelphia. They had been caught when young in the western part of Pennsylvania. The male was supposed to be four or five years old, and the female also was full grown. These Elks were transported to our place near New York, and we had a capacious and high enclosure made for them. The male retained much of its savage habits when at liberty, but the female was quite gentle. When she was first put in the pen, where the buck was already pacing around and seeking a weak point in the enclosure, he rushed towards her, and so terrified her that she made violent exertions to escape. She ran at full speed, her head up and nostrils distended, round and round, until we had the large box in which she had been brought up from Philadelphia placed in the enclosure. She entered it as a place of refuge, resorting to it whenever she wished to be undisturbed.

"We had difficulty in removing the buck's bridle, as he kicked and pranced furiously whenever anyone approached, and we were forced to secure his head by means of a lasso over his horns, drawing him by main force to a strong post, where one of our men cut the bridle with a knife. These Elks were fed on green oats, hay, Indian corn. They ate as much as would have sufficed for two horses. They often whistled, as the hunters call this remarkable noise which, in calm weather, can be heard nearly a mile.

"The teeth are much prized by the Indians to ornament their dresses. A 'queen's robe' presented to us is decorated with the teeth of fifty-six Elks.[21] This splendid garment, made of Antelope skins, was valued at no less than thirty horses!"

—*Quads. Vol. II, pp. 87–88, 89, 90, 92.*

Fig. 51. BARREN GROUND CARIBOU *(page 122)*

"The Caribou is one of the most important animals of the northern parts of America, and is almost as graceful in form as the Elk, to which it is nearly equal in size. But it has never, we believe, been domesticated or trained to draw sledges in the manner of the Reindeer of the old world, although so nearly allied to that species that it has been by most authors considered identical with it.

"The Caribou is famous for its swiftness, and has various gaits, walking, trotting or galloping alike gracefully and rapidly. By many people these animals are in fact thought to be much fleeter than the Moose, and they are said to take most extraordinary leaps."

—*Quads. Vol. III, pp. 113–114.*

Fig. 52. MOOSE *(page 123)*

"This is the largest of any known species of Deer. Although the Moose swim well they are not known to dive; they swim with the head and part of the neck above water like cattle. When pursued in boats they frequently attempt to upset them, and at times open their mouths and make a loud snorting noise, striking at the same time with their forefeet, and occasionally sinking the canoes of the Indians or hunters. On one occasion a young man, going fishing and having his fowling-piece along, saw a large Moose in the lake and fired at it. The Moose at once made for the canoe, and while the alarmed fisherman was attempting to escape, his boat became entangled in the branches of a fallen tree. He was forced to give up the canoe and get away as best he could. The animal, on reaching the boat, completely demolished it."

—*Quads. Vol. II, pp. 179, 187.*

Fig. 53. PRONG-HORNED ANTELOPE *(page 124)*

"Let us carry you with us to the boundless plains over which the Prong-horn speeds. Hurrah for the prairies and the swift Antelopes as they flee from the hunter like flashes or meteors, seen but for an instant. Observe now a flock of these beautiful animals. They are not afraid of man—they pause to gaze on the hunter, and stand with head erect, their ears as well as eyes directed towards him, and make a loud noise by stamping their forefeet on the hard earth. But suddenly they become aware that he is no friend, and away they bound and disappear, perhaps again to come into view and gaze at the intruder.

"While in the far West in 1843 we had the pleasure of seeing an old female in a flock of eight or ten Antelopes, suckling its young. The little beauty performed this operation precisely in the manner of our common lambs. Almost kneeling, and bending its head upwards, its rump elevated, it thumped the bag of its mother from time to time, and reminded us of far distant scenes where no prowling Wolf or hungry Indian defeats the hopes of the shepherd who nightly folds his stock of the Leicester or Bakewell breed. Our wild Antelopes scampered away as we approached them, and we were delighted to see first—and in the van of all—the young one!"

—*Quads. Vol. II, pp. 195–196, 199.*

Fig. 54. ROCKY MOUNTAIN BIGHORN *(page 125)*

"It was on June 12th, 1843, that we first saw this remarkable animal. We were near the confluence of the Yellowstone river with the Missouri when a group of them, twenty-two in all, came in sight."

—*Quads. Vol. II, p. 165.*

From the Missouri River Journal, August 13, 1843:

". . . No one who has not seen the Mauvaises Terres, or Bad Lands, can form any idea of these resorts of the Rocky Mountain Rams, or the difficulty of approaching these animals. They form paths around the broken-headed cones which are from three to fifteen hundred feet high, and run round them at full speed on a track that does not, to the eye of the hunter, appear to be more than a few

---

[21] On exhibition in American Museum of Natural History.

inches wide. The Bighorn is often seen looking on the hunter far below, and standing immovable as a statue. No one can imagine how they reach these places, and with their young, even when these are quite small. Hunters say that the young are usually born in such places, the mothers going there to save the helpless little ones from the Wolves, which, after men, seem to be their greatest destroyers.

"It is no light task to follow the Bighorns through these lands, and the pursuit is attended with much danger, as the least slip would at times send one headlong into the ravines below. Moreover, venomous snakes of many kinds are found here. I saw, myself, only one copperhead and a common garter-snake. Notwithstanding the rough country, the Buffaloes have paths running in all directions. Quite as agile as the European Chamois, they [Bighorns] leap down precipices, across ravines, and run up and down almost perpendicular hills. From the character of the lands where they are found, their own shyness, watchfulness and agility, it is readily seen what the hunter must undergo to near these 'Wild Goats.'"

Fig. 55. ROCKY MOUNTAIN GOAT (page 126)

"The Rocky Mountain Goat wanders over the most precipitous rocks, springing from crag to crag, feeding on the plants, grasses and mosses of the mountainsides, seldom if ever descending to the luxuriant valleys as the Big Horn does.

"Standing 'at gaze,' on a table-rock projecting high above the valley beyond, and with a lofty ridge of stony and precipitous mountains in the background, we have placed one of our figures of the Rocky Mountain Goat; and lying down, a little removed from the edge of the cliff, we have represented another.

"In the vast ranges of wild and desolate heights, alternating with deep valleys and tremendous gorges, well named the Rocky mountains, over and through which the adventurous trapper makes his way in pursuit of the rich fur of the Beaver or the hide of the Bison, there are scenes which the soul must be dull indeed not to admire. In these majestic solitudes all is on a scale to awaken the sublimest emotions and fill the heart with a consciousness of the infinite Being 'whose temple is all space, whose altar earth, sea, skies.'

"Lewis and Clark obtained skins in 1804. M. De Blainville published the first scientific account of it in 1816."

—*Quads. Vol. III, pp. 129, 130, 131, 132.*

Fig. 56. MUSK OX (page 127)

"We know this peculiar animal only from the specimen in the British Museum, from which our figures were drawn, and which is the only one hitherto sent to Europe, so difficult is it to procure in a tolerable state of preservation from the northern portions of British America. An almost perpetual winter and consequent scarcity of food make it difficult to prevent the Indians, or white hunters, from eating (we should say devouring) everything that can fill their empty stomachs—even skins, hoofs and the most unsavory parts of any animal they kill.

"Sir George Simpson, of the Hudson's Bay Fur Company, most kindly promised that he would if possible procure a skin of the Musk Ox for the completion of our work. We have not yet received his promised skin ... Among the difficulties and worries of such a publication as the *Quadrupeds*, it has been gratifying to have the sympathies and assistance of such gentlemen, and of so powerful a corporation as the Hudson's Bay Fur Company.

"The Musk Ox is remarkable among the animals of America for never having had more than one specific name. Jeremie appears to have given the first notice of it. He brought some of the wool to France, and had stockings more beautiful than silk made of it. Captain Parry saw it on Melville Island in the month of May; it must therefore be regarded as an animal the native home of which is within the Arctic Circle, the dwelling place of the Esquimaux."

—*Quads. Vol. III, pp. 48, 49, 52.*

Figs. 57 and 58. AMERICAN BISON OR BUFFALO (pages 128, 129)

"This noble animal is decidedly the most important of all our contemporary American quadrupeds. We can no longer see the gigantic mastodon; but we will consider the Buffalo as a link which yet connects us, to a slight degree, with larger American animals now extinct.

"A large Bison bull will generally weigh nearly two thousand pounds, and a fat cow about twelve hundred.

"One day we landed on one of the narrow strips of land forming the margin of the Missouri, backed by nearby hills. The buffalo tracks were literally innumerable; the plain was covered with them. Their great tracks, resembling large wagon tracks, run for hundreds of miles across the prairies to some watering place.

"Some idea of the immense number of Bisons still to be seen in the wild prairies may be formed from an account given us by one of the American Fur Company officers. While he was travelling from Travers' Bay to the nation of the Mandan Indians in his cart, he passed through herds of Buffalo for six days in succession. Another time he saw the great prairie near Fort Clark on the Missouri almost blackened by these animals, which covered the plain to the hills that bounded the view in all directions."

—*Quads. Vol. II, pp. 35, 47.*

Figs. 59 and 60. AMERICAN HARE (pages 130, 131)

"In summer the whole of the upper surface is reddish brown [Fig. 60]. During the winter it becomes nearly pure white [Fig. 59]. During summer it seems to prefer dry and elevated situations, grounds covered with pines and fir. The swamps and marshes soil their feet, and for hours they are employed in rubbing and drying their paws. In winter, when such places are hardened by frost, they have paths through them in every direction, and occasionally seek a fallen tree-top as a hiding or resting place, in the center of a swamp."

—*Quads. Vol. I, pp. 94, 99.*

Fig. 61. PIKA OR LITTLE CHIEF HARE (page 132)

"It affords us pleasure to quote from a letter received from Mr. Nuttall:

" 'I first discovered it by its peculiar cry, far up the mountain of the dividing ridge between the waters of the Columbia and Colorado, and the Missouri, hiding among loose piles of rocks. From this retreat I heard a slender but very distinct bleat, like

that of a young kid or Goat. But in vain I tried to discover any large animal around me. At length, I may almost literally say, the mountain brought forth nothing much larger than a mouse, as I discovered that this little animal was the real author of the unexpected note.' "

—*Quads. Vol. II, p. 247.*

Fig. 62. ARCTIC HARE (page 132)

"In winter the Arctic Hare is entirely white except for the tips of the ears. In summer its color is grayish brown, ears black bordered with white, neck and breast bluish-gray. Changes of color conceal it from its enemies.

"It is to the cold and inhospitable regions of Labrador, and the wild mountainsides of that desolate land, or the yet wilder countries from thence west, that we must resort to find this large and beautiful Hare.

"Captain Ross states, 'One taken by us a few days after its birth soon became tame enough to eat from our hands, and was allowed to run loose about the cabin. During the summer we fed it on plants, and in winter on grass and astragali, but it preferred to share whatever our table could afford, and would enjoy pea soup, plum pudding, bread, barley, soup, sugar, rice, and even cheese with us. It could not endure to be caressed, but was exceedingly fond of company, and would sit for hours listening to a conversation, which was no sooner ended than it would retire to its cabin. It was a continual source of amusement by its sagacity and playfulness.' "

—*Quads. Vol. I, pp. 243, 247.*

Fig. 63. CALIFORNIA BRUSH RABBIT (page 133)

"This Rabbit so much resembles the Common Rabbit that it has been generally considered the same animal, but its specific characters are now fully established."

—*Quads. Vol. III, p. 37.*

Fig. 64. SWAMP RABBIT (page 133)

"The habits of this animal are singular, differing in one remarkable peculiarity from those of any other species of hare yet known, with the exception of the Swamp Rabbit. Though occasionally seen on high grounds in dense forest, it prefers low and marshy places, and swims with great facility from one islet to another."

—Quads. Vol. I, pp. 288–289.

Fig. 65. MARSH RABBIT (page 134)

"The Marsh Rabbit is generally found in low marsh grounds, near rivers subject to freshets that occasionally overflow their banks, or near large ponds. In these situations—surrounded by frogs, watersnakes and alligators—this species lives throughout the year, rarely molested by man, and enabled by its aquatic habits to make up for any want of speed in eluding its enemies. But for the miry, tangled and thorny character of its usual haunts, it would soon be overtaken, it is so slow of foot."

—Quads. Vol. I, pp. 152–153.

Fig. 66. CALIFORNIA BLACK-TAILED JACK "RABBIT" (page 135)

"Startled, he is as wild as a Deer and equally heedless of his course, so that (as he has not the Deer's keen sense of smell to warn of danger) he sometimes makes a great fool of himself in his haste. I have had him run to within three feet of me before he saw me, even where there was no cover but sparse prairie grass. It was after toiling night and day through the sands of the Colorado desert, and resting afterwards at Vallecitos and San Felipe, while marching along the streams through the rich fields of Santa Maria, that I saw this Rabbit. I knew him at sight."

—Quads. Vol. III, pp. 54–55.

Fig. 67. WHITE-TAILED JACK "RABBIT" (page 136)

" 'Immediately after we arrived at Walla in the Rockies,' wrote J. K. Townsend, 'we were regaled with a dish of Rabbit, and I thought I had never eaten anything more delicious. They are found in great numbers on the plains, and are so exceedingly fleet no ordinary dog can catch them.' "

—Quads. Vol. I, p. 28.

From the Missouri River Journal, June 9, 1843:

"A Negro fire-tender went off with his rifle and shot two Rabbits. I have one hanging before me, and let me tell you that I never before saw so beautiful an animal of the same family. My drawing will be a good one; it is a fine specimen, an old male."

Fig. 68. TEXAS JACK "RABBIT" (page 137)

"Our troops in the Mexican war named this the 'Jackass Rabbit.' Fabulous stories have been told us of this Rabbit, which was described to us as equal to a Fox in size. We were somewhat disappointed when we procured it, although it *is* a fine large species. Among old stories is a curious one in Clavigero's notes elucidated by Dr. Hernandez: 'When it has killed any game, it climbs a tree and utters a howl of invitation to other animals. They come, eat, and die, because the flesh was poisoned by the Rabbit's bite. It descends from the tree and makes a meal from the quarry that its trick has put at its disposal.' "

—Quads. Vol. III, pp. 157, 158.

Fig. 69. TEXAS JACK "RABBIT" (page 138)

"At Castroville, a little Texas settlement of about a dozen huts and one house, this Rabbit was brought by a party of Indians and brought to John Woodhouse Audubon, who wrote in his journal:

" 'I chanced to be visited by some Shawnee Indians who were in the neighborhood on a hunting expedition. They were highly astonished and pleased with my drawings, which I showed them while trying to explain what animals I wanted. I made a hasty sketch of a hare with immensely long ears, at which I pointed with an approving nod, and then made another sketch smaller and with shorter ears, at which last I shook my head and made wry faces. The Indians laughed, and in a day or two I had a beautiful specimen of the Black-tailed Rabbit brought to me.

" 'This rare species is called the "Jackass Rabbit" in Texas, owing to the length of its ears. Since the Mexican war broke out, several have been sent home by our officers.' "

—*Quads. Vol. II, p. 98.*

Fig. 70. COTTONTAIL OR GRAY RABBIT (page 139)

"This being the most common Rabbit in the Atlantic States of America, it has been longest and most familiarly known. Herriott, who gave an account of the third voyage of the English to Virginia in 1586, mentioned it under the head of Conies.

"At the house of Dr. De Benneville at Milestown, near Philadelphia, we saw five or six that were taken from the nest when very young, so completely tamed that they came at the call and leapt upon the lap of the feeder. They lived sociably among the dogs and poultry. Although accustomed to chase the wild Rabbit, the dogs never molested them. We have not only observed dogs peacefully associating with the Rabbit, when thus tamed, but have seen hounds eating from the same platter with the Deer that was domesticated and loose in the yard, even defending it from the attacks of strange dogs that came on the premises. And when this tame Deer, which occasionally visited the woods, was started by the pack of hounds here referred to, they refused to pursue it."

—*Quads. Vol. I, pp. 176, 179.*

Figs. 71 and 72. WASHINGTON ROCKY MOUNTAIN COTTONTAIL RABBIT (pages 140, 141)

(Page 140)

"Mr. Nuttall's note which accompanied the specimen states: 'This little Rabbit we met with west of the Rocky Mountains, inhabiting thickets by the banks of several small streams which flow into the Shoshone and Columbia rivers. It was frequently seen in the evening about our encampment.' "

—*Quads. Vol. II, p. 301.*

(Page 141)

"Mr. Townsend who procured it at Fort Wallawalla remarks: 'It is here abundant but very shy keeping constantly in the densest wormwood bushes, and leaping with singular speed from pursuit.' "

—*Quads. Vol. II, p. 273.*

Fig. 73. GRAY SQUIRREL (page 142)

"This Squirrel was drawn from the skin in the museum of the Zoological Society of London, and the description was published by the Society in its Proceedings in 1839."

—*Quads. Vol. III, p. 76.*

Fig. 74. EASTERN GRAY SQUIRREL OR CAROLINA GRAY SQUIRREL (page 143)

"We have observed the Carolina Gray Squirrel on several occasions by moonlight, as actively engaged as the Flying Squirrel usually is in the evening. This propensity to prolong its search for food or its playful gambols causes it frequently to fall a prey to the Great Horned Owl or the Barred Owl in the swamps of the Carolinas, where, gliding on noiseless pinions between the leafy branches, it seizes the luckless Squirrel."

—*Quads. Vol. I, p. 58.*

Fig. 75. EASTERN GRAY SQUIRREL (page 144)

"We have represented in the plate three of these Squirrels, all of different colors. The varieties to be observed are so great that among fifty or more we never could find two exactly alike. This Squirrel is the most inactive of all our known species. It climbs a tree, not with the lightness of the Northern Gray Squirrel, but with the apparent reluctance of the little Striped Squirrel. We have seldom observed it leaping from bough to bough."

—*Quads. Vol. I, p. 147.*

Figs. 76 and 77. NORTHERN GRAY SQUIRREL (pages 145, 146)

"This appears to be the most active and sprightly species of Squirrel in our Atlantic States. It has occasionally excited wonder by its wandering habits and its singular and long migrations. Like the Lemming it is stimulated either by scarcity of food or by some other inexplicable instinct to leave its native haunts. The newspapers from the West contain many interesting details of these migrations, more frequent in former years. The farmers in the Western wilds regard them with sensations comparable to those inspired by the devouring locust. Onward the Squirrels come, devouring everything suited to their taste, laying waste the corn and wheat fields. As their numbers are thinned by gun, dog and club, others fall in and fill up the ranks. How do they cross broad rivers? It is believed by many people that they carry a piece of bark to the shore and seat themselves on this substitute for a boat, hoist their broad tails as a sail, and float safely to the opposite shore. This we suspect to be apocryphal. It has appeared to us that they are not only unskilful sailors but clumsy swimmers. In the autumn of 1808 or 1809 troops of Squirrels appeared suddenly in the neighborhood, among them varieties not seen in these parts. They swam the Hudson at various places between Waterford and Saratoga. Those which we saw crossing the river were swimming deep and awkwardly, their bodies and tails wholly submerged. Their migrations did not, as far as we could learn, extend east of the mountains of Vermont. Many remained in Rensselaer County, New York. It is doubtful whether any ever return to the West. They take up permanent residence in their newly explored country until they are gradually thinned off by the increase of inhabitants and new clearings.

"When we were descending the Ohio in a flatboat in 1819, seeking for birds then unknown to us, we saw a large number of Squirrels about a hundred miles below Cincinnati, swimming across the river, strewn over the surface of the water."

—*Quads. Vol. I, pp. 267, 271–272.*

Fig. 78. WESTERN GRAY SQUIRREL *(page 147)*

"We have represented two of these Squirrels in our plate, on a branch of hickory, with a bunch of nearly ripe nuts attached. They were brought from California."

—*Quads. Vol. I, p. 330.*

Fig. 79. FOX SQUIRREL *(page 148)*

"This is the largest and most interesting species of the Squirrel in the United States. At times it takes possession of the hole of the Ivory-billed Woodpecker. The Wood Duck is frequently a competitor for the same residence, and contests take place. We have generally observed that the tenant that has already deposited its eggs or young is seldom ejected. The male and female duck unite in chasing and beating with their wings any Squirrel that may approach their nests, nor are they idle with their bills and tongues. On the other hand, when the Squirrel has its young in the hole of a tree and is intruded on, it immediately rushes to the hole, enters it, protrudes its head occasionally, and with a low angry bark keeps possession until the intruder wearies of the contest. Thus Nature imparts to each species additional spirit and vigor in defense of its young."

—*Quads. Vol. II, pp. 132, 135.*

Fig. 80. WESTERN FOX SQUIRREL *(page 149)*

"The forests on the rich bottom lands of the Wabash, the Illinois, and the Missouri rivers are ornamented with the stately pecan tree, on the nuts of which these Squirrels luxuriate. They also resort to the hickory and oak trees in the vicinity of their residence, as well as to the hazel bushes, on the fruits of which they feed."

—*Quads. Vol. II, p. 275.*

Fig. 81. WESTERN FOX SQUIRREL *(page 150)*

"In form this species resembles the Northern Gray Squirrel, possessing all its activity. Our drawing was made from one procured in Illinois."

—*Quads. Vol. II, p. 31.*

Fig. 82. WESTERN FOX SQUIRREL OR TEXAS FOX SQUIRREL *(page 151)*

"During the winter season the city of New Orleans is thronged by natives of almost every land, and the Levee presents a scene so unlike anything American that as we walk along its smooth surface we may imagine ourselves in some twenty different countries. Our eyes fall upon many a strange costume . . . here a Spanish gentleman from Cuba, or a Mexican, next a pirate or thief, perhaps, from the same countries. The language of many parts of the world can be heard. The descendants of Africa are here metamorphosed into French folks, and the gay bandanna that turbans the heads of the colored women is always adjusted with good taste. But the most interesting figures are the few straggling Choctaw and Chicasaw Indians, who bring a variety of game to the markets. In their blankets, red flannel leggings, moccasins and bead finery they form a sort of dirty picturesque feature in the motley scene, and generally attract the artist's eye. Whilst conversing with one of these remnants of a once numerous race, it was our good fortune to see for the first time this singular and beautiful little Squirrel which the Indian hunter had brought with other animals for sale, having got it in the recesses of the forest border—an extensive swamp."

—Quads. Vol. II, pp. 68–69.

Fig. 83 (top figure). FREMONT'S CHICKAREE OR PINE SQUIRREL (page 152)

"It feeds on the seeds of the pines, inhabits elevated regions, climbs, burrows in the ground, where it dwells in winter, utters the peculiar note *chickaree chickaree,* differing from the *qua qua quah* of the larger squirrels. Our specimen was obtained by Colonel Fremont on the Rocky Mountains."

—Quads. Vol. III, p. 238.

Fig. 83 (lower figure). BLACK FOX SQUIRREL (page 152)

"They feed chiefly on pecan nuts, and are deemed by the French inhabitants of Louisiana to be the most savory of all the Squirrels and are called by them *le petit noir.* The specimen for our description was obtained near New Orleans, March 24th, 1837."

—Quads. Vol. III, p. 241.

Fig. 84. COLLIE'S SQUIRREL (page 153)

"Our figures were made from the Squirrel presented to the Zoological Society of London by Captain Beechey. Mr. Collie observed it sporting on trees at San Blas in California."

—Quads. Vol. III, p. 22.

Fig. 85. VANCOUVER RED SQUIRREL (page 154)

"This downy and beautifully furred Squirrel exists in the northwestern portions of our continent. The specimen from which our drawing was made is the only one which we have seen, and was brought from near Sitka by J. K. Townsend, the naturalist, who kindly placed it in our hands that we might describe it. It was presented to him by an officer, W. F. Tolmie, Surgeon of the Honorable Hudson's Bay Company."

—Quads. Vol. I, p. 200.

Fig. 86. RICHARDSON'S RED SQUIRREL (page 155)

"A note from J. K. Townsend remarks: 'Not at all shy, they frequently come down to the foot of the tree to reconnoiter the passenger and scold him vociferously.' "

—Quads. Vol. I, p. 42.

Fig. 87. REDWOOD CHICKAREE OR RED SQUIRREL (page 156)

"Our specimens were obtained in northern California, near the Pacific Ocean."

—Quads. Vol. I, p. 158.

Fig. 88. EASTERN RED SQUIRREL OR CHICKAREE (page 157)

"Although you may find that more Squirrels inhabit our forests than you expected or desired to be figured in this work, we assure you that it would give us pleasure to discover a new species at any time! We hope you will find this really beautiful genus as interesting as any other among the quadrupeds we place before you."

—Quads. Vol. I, p. 127.

Fig. 89. DOUGLAS'S CHICKAREE (page 158)

"Our specimens were procured from the northern and mountainous portions of California. A figure of each is given on the plate."

—Quads. Vol. I, p. 215.

Fig. 90. DOUGLAS'S CHICKAREE (page 159)

"Our specimens were procured by J. K. Townsend, who remarks in his notes: 'This very plentiful species inhabits the pine trees along the shores of the Columbia River.' Douglas obtained his specimens in the Rocky Mountains."

—Quads. Vol. I, p. 371.

Fig. 91. RED-BELLIED SQUIRREL (page 160)

"Several specimens, differing a little in color, which differences we have represented in our plate, were received from California."

—Quads. Vol. I, p. 293.

Fig. 92. EASTERN FLYING SQUIRREL (page 161)

"We can say for ourselves that on many occasions when studying inferior creatures, we have felt that we were reading lessons taught us by nature, calculated to make us wiser and better. Often, while straying in the fields and woods with a book under our arm, have we been tempted to leave Homer or Aristotle unopened, and attend to the teachings of the quadrupeds and birds. Even the gentle little Flying Squirrel has more than once diverted our attention from the pages, and taught us lessons of contentment, innocence, and parental and filial affection, more impressive than theological disquisitions.

"We recollect a locality near Philadelphia where, in order to study this interesting species, we occasionally strayed into a meadow containing immense oak and beech trees. One afternoon in the beginning of autumn we took our seat on a log to watch their lively motions. The birds had retired to the forest. The Night-Hawk had already commenced his low evening flight. Here and there the common Red Bat was on the wing. Still, for some time, not a Flying Squirrel appeared. Suddenly one emerged from its hole; another soon followed, and ere long dozens came forth and commenced their graceful flights from branch to bough. One would dart from the topmost branches of a tall oak, and with wide-

N.B. See also Squirrels, pages 190, 191, 214.

extended membranes and outspread tail glide diagonally through the air to the foot of a tree about fifty yards off. At the moment we expected to see it strike the earth it suddenly turned upwards and alighted on the body of the tree, then sailed back again to the tree it had just left. Crowds of these little creatures joined in these sportive gambols—there could not have been less than two hundred gliding like spirits."

—Quads. Vol. I, pp. 217–218.

Fig. 93. OLYMPIC FLYING SQUIRREL (page 162)

"Much do we regret that we have never seen this handsome Flying Squirrel launch itself into the air, and sail from the highest branch of one of the enormous pines of the valley of the Columbia river to some tall, magnificent tree. Indeed, much should we like to know the many works of the Creator that yet remain to be discovered, examined, figured, and described, in the vast mountain valleys and forests beyond the peaks of the great Rocky Chain."

—Quads. Vol. I, p. 134.

Fig. 94 (lower figure). NORTHERN FLYING SQUIRREL (page 163)

"We found this Severn River Flying Squirrel in abundance at Quebec, and many were offered for sale in the markets."

—Quads. Vol. III, p. 203.

Fig. 94 (upper figure). RICHARDSON'S FLYING SQUIRREL (page 163)

"This Flying Squirrel lives in pine forests, seldom venturing from its retreats except during the night."

—Quads. Vol. III, p. 207.

Fig. 95. EASTERN CHIPMUNK (page 164)

"The Chipmunk is probably, with the exception of the common Flying Squirrel, one of the most interesting of our small quadrupeds. We have a specimen now lying before us, sent from Pennsylvania in alcohol, which contains at least one and a half tablespoonful of Bush trefoil in its widely distended sacks. We have represented one of our figures in the plate with pouches thus filled out.

"In 1838 we carried American specimens to Europe and were surprised at finding none in the museums of England or France. But in Berlin's museum we were permitted to open the cases and examine several, to compare them with our American species, which we placed beside them."

—*Quads. Vol. I, pp. 67, 69, 74–75.*

Fig. 96. SAY'S CHIPMUNK *(page 165)*

"We met with this species as we were descending the Upper Missouri river in 1843. We saw it first on a tree. Afterwards we procured both old and young among the sandy gulleys and clay cliffs on the sides of the ravines near one of our encampments. It was originally discovered by Say on the Rocky Mountains, near the sources of the Arkansas and Platte rivers.

"The investigation of described species in every branch of natural history, both in Europe and America, occupied much of the time of the naturalists of our generation, who corrected many of the errors of a former age. Most fortunate are they who are permitted to live to correct their own."

—*Quads. Vol. I, pp. 197–198.*

Fig. 97. THIRTEEN-STRIPED GROUND SQUIRREL *(page 165)*

"In the warm days of spring, the traveller on our Western prairies is often diverted from the contemplation of larger animals to watch the movements of this lively little species. He withdraws his attention from the bellowing Buffalo herd to fix his eyes on a lively creature of exquisite beauty seated on a diminutive mound at the mouth of its burrow. It darts into its hole, but, concealed from view, and out of the reach of danger, its tongue is not idle. It continues to vent its threats of resentment against its unwelcome visitor by a shrill and harsh repetition of the word *seek—seek*.

"We found it quite abundant near Fort Union, on the Upper Missouri.

"Among the quadrupeds, there are innumerable varieties of form and character; and although most animals are nocturnal, and therefore their habits cannot be studied with the same facility with which the manners and customs of the lively diurnal species of birds may be observed; yet when we follow them in their nightly wanderings, penetrate into their retreats, and observe the sagacity and extraordinary instincts with which they are endowed, we find in them matter to interest us greatly, and arouse our curiosity and astonishment.

"Owls seem to us a dull and stupid race, principally because we only notice them during the day, which nature requires them to spend in sleep, the structure of their eyes compelling them to avoid the light, and seek concealment in hollow trees, in caves, and obscure retreats. But we should recollect that the diurnal birds are, during night, the time for their repose, as dull and stupid as owls are during the day. We should therefore not judge the habits of quadrupeds by the same standard. In regard to their fur, and external markings, there are many that will strike even the most careless observer as eminently beautiful."

—*Quads. Vol. I, pp. 296, 297, 298.*

Fig. 98. TOWNSEND'S CHIPMUNK *(page 166)*

"Mr. Townsend, who procured the specimens, observes, 'This pretty little fellow is quite common, and lives in holes in the ground, running over your foot as you traverse the woods. It frequently perches itself on a log or stump, and keeps up a continual clucking, usually answered at some distance.' This note so much resembles that of the dusky Grouse that I have more than once been deceived by it."

—*Quads. Vol. I, pp. 160–161.*

Fig. 99. SAY'S MANTLED GROUND SQUIRREL *(page 167)*

"The Mexican women make pets of some of these lively Ground Squirrels inhabiting their country. They become very fond of their mistresses, running over their shoulders, and, sometimes, nestling in their bosoms or in the pockets of their gowns."

—*Quads. Vol. III, p. 64.*

Fig. 100. RICHARDSON'S GROUND SQUIRREL
(page 168)

"Our specimens were obtained from Mr. Townsend, and we are indebted to the excellent work of Richardson for a description of its habits."
—*Quads. Vol. I, p. 378.*

Fig. 101. HUDSON BAY GROUND SQUIRREL
(page 168)

"Our description is drawn up from a specimen in the museum of the Zoological Society of London. Captain Ross writes from Hudson's Bay that some of the dresses of the Esquimaux at Repulse Bay were made of the skins of this species. The people informed him that it was very abundant in that inhospitable region."
—*Quads. Vol. I, pp. 79, 80.*

Figs. 102 and 103. MEXICAN GROUND SQUIRREL (page 169)

"When caught alive this pretty species makes a pet of no common attractions, having beautiful eyes and being very handsomely marked. Its disposition soon becomes affectionate, and it retains its gay and frolicsome habits, eats corn and seeds, is fond of bits of potato, apple, or any kind of fruit, as well as bread, pastry, cakes, and any kind of vegetable food. We had a fine living animal of this species in a cage, and he was a source of great amusement to the little folks, who were pleased with his antics. They are said to be tolerably abundant in Mexico and California, but only in the wooded districts."
—*Quads. Vol. III, pp. 40–41.*

Fig. 104. MEXICAN ROCK SQUIRREL
(page 169)

"This Squirrel exists in some portions of the part of Mexico traversed by J. W. Audubon on his way towards California, where it is also found."
—*Quads. Vol. III, p. 183.*

Fig. 105. RING-TAILED GROUND SQUIRREL
(page 170)

"Our specimen was obtained on the Western prairies, we believe on the east of the Mississippi river, and presented to us by Professor Spencer F. Baird of Carlisle, Pennsylvania, a young naturalist of eminent attainments."
—*Quads. Vol. II, p. 215.*

Fig. 106. DOUGLAS'S GROUND SQUIRREL
(page 170)

"J. K. Townsend, the naturalist, loaned us four specimens, from which we made our drawing. One is marked 'Falls of the Columbia River,' another 'Walla-Walla.' "
—*Quads. Vol. I, p. 375.*

Fig. 107. FRANKLIN'S SPERMOPHILE
(page 171)

"This is a northern and western species. Townsend obtained it near the Columbia river."
—*Quads. Vol. II, p. 250.*

Fig. 108. BLACK-TAILED PRAIRIE DOG
(page 171)

"This Prairie Dog was seen by John Woodhouse Audubon in Sonora and on the sandy hills adjoining the Tulare Valley, and in other parts of California. It is probably only owing to the sort of yelp, *chip, chip, chip,* uttered by this species, that they were called Prairie *Dogs.* The first of their villages seen by our party was near 'the Great Bend' of the Missouri in 1843.

"Kendall's *Narrative of the Texan Santa Fe Expedition* gives an amusing account of a large village of Prairie Dogs: 'On several occasions I crept close to their village to watch their movements. Directly in the center of one village I particularly noticed a very large Dog, sitting in front of the door to his burrow. By his own actions and those of his neighbors it really seemed as though he was the president, mayor, or chief—the "big Dog" of the place.

He received at least a dozen visits from his fellow Dogs during the hour that I watched. They would stop and chat with him a few moments, then run off to their domiciles. All this while he never left his post for a moment, and I thought I could discover a gravity in his deportment not discernible in those around him. Far be it from me to say that those visits he received were on business, or had anything to do with the local government of the village. But it certainly appeared so. If any animal has a system of laws regulating the body politic, it is the Prairie Dog.'"

—*Quads. Vol. II, pp. 320, 323–324, 326.*

Fig. 109. WHITE-TAILED PRAIRIE DOG (page 171)

"The specimen from which our figure was made, and which we believe to be the only one in any collection, was sent to the Zoological Society by the British fur traders who annually carry their peltry down the Columbia to the Pacific."

—*Quads. Vol. III, p. 33.*

Fig. 110. YELLOW-BELLIED MARMOT (page 172)

"The specimen from which our description was made was found by us among the skins sent to England by Drummond and Douglas, from our northwestern territories. The skin is now set up in the museum of the Zoological Society of London."

—*Quads. Vol. III, p. 161.*

Fig. 111. HOARY MARMOT (page 173)

"We examined a live Hoary Marmot at the Zoological Gardens in London. Our drawing was made from one in the Museum of the Zoological Society there; the Marmot had died in the Menagerie gardens in Regent's Park. It was obtained on Captain Back's expedition. The first specimen was brought to England from Hudson's Bay, and it excited much interest, as its existence had for many years been doubted."

—*Quads. Vol. III, pp. 19, 20.*

Fig. 112. EASTERN WOODCHUCK (page 174)

"The Woodchuck may be said to have no winter in its year, but enjoys the delightful weather of spring, summer and autumn, without caring for the approach of that season during which other animals often suffer from cold and hunger."

—*Quads. Vol. I, p. 21.*

Fig. 113. BEAVER (page 175)

"The sagacity and instinct of the Beaver have from time immemorial been the subject of admiration and wonder. The early writers on both continents have represented it as a rational, intelligent and moral being, requiring but the faculty of speech to raise it almost to an equality, in some respects, with our own species. We are now almost led to regret that three-fourths of the old accounts of this extraordinary animal are fabulous, and that in point of intelligence and cunning the Beaver is greatly exceeded by the Fox, and but a few grades higher than the Muskrat in the scale of sagacity.

"It is a curious fact, says our trapper, that there are some that are lazy and will not work at all, either to assist in building lodges or dams, or to cut down wood for their winter stock. The industrious ones beat these idle fellows and drive them away. These idlers are more easily trapped than the others. They never form dams. All are males. It is not at all improbable that these unfortunate fellows have been engaged in fighting with others of their sex, and, after having been conquered and driven away from the lodge, have become idlers from a kind of necessity. The working Beavers associate, on the contrary—males, females and young together.

"The Beavers usually go to the dam every evening to see if repairs are needed. They rarely travel by land, unless their dams have been carried away by the ice, and even then they take the beds of the rivers or streams for their roadway."

—*Quads. Vol. I, pp. 349, 352.*

Fig. 114. SEWELLEL OR MOUNTAIN BEAVER (page 175)

"Lewis and Clark discovered this species during their journey across the Rocky Mountains and gave an account of it: 'Sewellel is a name given by the natives to a small animal found in the timbered country on this Coast. The natives make great use of the skins for robes. This animal mounts a tree and burrows in the ground, precisely like the squirrel.' Our figure was drawn from a fine specimen in London."

—*Quads. Vol. III, p. 101.*

Fig. 115. PINE VOLE *(page 176)*

"This Vole is an inhabitant of cultivated fields rather than of woods, claiming a share of the gleanings of the fields before the crops are gathered."
—*Quads. Vol. II, p. 217.*

Fig. 116 *(left)*. RICHARDSON'S VOLE *(page 176)*

"All meadow Voles indeed are capital swimmers. We once amused ourselves watching one that had fallen into a cistern. On a dry stone knob above the water we saw a Vole seated quietly. It had probably tumbled in the night before. When we approached we did not see it at first, but as soon as it saw us, it immediately dived and swam rapidly under the surface. It resumed its position on the ledge, and we determined to save it from drowning, starving, or both. Taking a plank we gently lowered one end towards it. The plank slipped and it made as pretty a dive as need be into the water, then returned to the ledge. As we fixed the plank and had it about three feet above the surface it dashed off again into the water. Again on the plank, it cast inquisitive looks towards us, appearing to have strong doubts of our intentions. After this attempt succeeded and it had reached the top of the cistern, it disappeared in a moment amid the grasses."
—*Quads. Vol. III, pp. 164–165.*

Fig. 116 *(right)*. DRUMMOND'S VOLE *(page 176)*

"Our drawing was made in the museum of the Zoological Society of London."
—*Quads. Vol. III, p. 167.*

Fig. 117. YELLOW-CHEEKED VOLE *(page 176)*

"The specimens brought by us from Labrador were obtained from beneath large masses of moss growing on the rocks, where they were abundant."
—*Quads. Vol. III, p. 68.*

Fig. 118 *(left)*. TOWNSEND'S GROUND SQUIRREL *(page 177)*

"This Squirrel exists on the western sides of the Rocky Mountains in Oregon, where the few specimens we have seen have been obtained. We carried one with us to Europe, and compared it with specimens from Siberia in the Berlin Museum."
—*Quads. Vol. III, pp. 227, 228.*

Fig. 118 *(right)*. TEXAS COTTON RAT *(page 177)*

"This active, pugnacious little Rat is sometimes seen in the edges of the chaparrals, where it nests in Texas."
—*Quads. Vol. III, p. 230.*

Fig. 118 *(center)*. OREGON VOLE *(page 177)*

"This Vole was captured in Oregon near the Columbia river."
—*Quads, Vol. III, p. 233.*

Fig. 119. RICHARDSON'S LEMMING *(page 177)*

"This species was found in numbers at Great Bear Lake."
—*Quads. Vol. III, p. 135.*

Fig. 120 *(left and center)*. AMERICAN LEMMING *(page 177)*

"This Lemming was found in the spring season at Great Bear Lake by Sir John Franklin of the Hudson's Bay Company."
—*Quads. Vol. III, p. 87.*

Fig. 120 (right). TAWNY LEMMING (page 177)

"Our figure of the Tawny Lemming was drawn from a skin in London by J. W. Audubon."

—Quads. Vol. III, p. 85.

Fig. 121. COLLARED LEMMING (page 178)

"We first saw this species in the museum of the Royal College of Surgeons in Edinburgh. Our drawing was made from specimens in the British Museum."

—Quads. Vol. III, p. 83.

Fig. 122. MEADOW JUMPING MOUSE (page 178)

"We doubt whether there is any quadruped of its size in the world that can make its way over the ground as rapidly. The ploughman in the Northern and Middle states sometimes turns it up from under a clod, and it immediately begins its long leaps in an irregular zig-zag direction, like the flying-fish at sea, as he drops his reins and hurries after it till it is out of sight, hidden behind a clod or in a tuft of grass."

—Quads. Vol. II, p. 253.

Fig. 123. HOUSE MOUSE (page 178)

"We have shown a shelf in a pantry, on which stands a china jar with indigo-blue peaked mountains, its fantastic trees and its rather remarkable landscapes reminding us more of the sweetmeats in it than of aught in the way of nature. We have also portrayed a plate with a piece of hard old cheese in it, on which a Mouse is standing in the act of listening. Another in the place, and two more on the shelf, likewise appear a little startled, and are expecting to be disturbed ere they can have their meal. The little rascals have reason to fear, for the careful housekeeper has heard them of late, squealing in their squabblings with one another, and has found the marks of their teeth, and is determined to be rid of them 'instanter' if possible. She is calling now to her faithful pussy cat and inquiring for the trap.

"But although the thieving Mouse is often frightened, and may be said to eat his dinner with 'a cat' over his head, although he is assailed with pokers and broomsticks as often as his death can be compassed by man's ingenuity or by the cunning of his ally, the cat, the Mouse will not retire from the house. Would he let drawings and books alone we should willingly allow him the crumbs from our table. Many a young lady will scream at the sight of a poor little Mouse, and many a brave young man might be startled in the stillness of the night by the noise made by this diminutive creature, especially if he is given to reading the *Mysteries of Udolpho* or the *Castle of Otranto* late in the hours of darkness, alone in a large old lumbering house.

"The activity, agility, and grace of the Mouse have made it a favorite pet with the prisoner in his solitary cell, and it has been known to answer his call and come out of hiding to play, and to eat out of his hand without fear. Of late years white Mice have been in demand in London, where they are taught various tricks and exhibited by boys in the streets.

"The Common Mouse is not a native of America, but of all countries where ships land cargo. It was brought to our shores with the early immigrants."

—Quads. Vol. II, pp. 278–279, 280.

Fig. 124. EASTERN WHITE-FOOTED MOUSE (page 179)

"Dr. Leitner, an eminent botanist, informed us that while on a botanizing tour in Florida he was frequently kept awake at night by these Mice, which had taken possession of the huts of the Indians and the log cabins of the white settlers. We are under the impression that the Norway Rat and the Common Cat were both absent. Farmers and gardeners of the Northern and Eastern states complain that this Mouse, which they generally call the 'Deer Mouse,' destroys many of their vegetables and gnaws the bark from young fruit trees."

—Quads. Vol. I, pp. 304, 305.

Fig. 125. HARVEST MOUSE (page 179)

"This diminutive species is rare. After a search of twenty years we have obtained only a dozen specimens from the fields. We doubt that it does much injury to the grains of the farmer. The female specimen from which our description was taken was the largest of any we have seen, containing four young in its matrix."

—Quads. Vol. II, pp. 104, 105.

Fig. 126. COMMON MEADOW MOUSE (page 179)

"We doubt whether this active little creature ever does much injury to the meadows. Still, we have to relate some of its habits that are not calculated to win the affections of the farmer. In severe winters it resorts for a subsistence to the stems of shrubs and fruit trees. We possessed a small but choice nursery which we had grafted ourselves that was completely destroyed by this Meadow Mouse."

—Quads. Vol. I, p. 343.

Fig. 127. SOUTHERN GOLDEN MOUSE (page 180)

"This is the prettiest species of Mouse inhabiting our country. A great climber, it runs up tall trees with agility, sometimes concealing itself in a hole thirty feet from the ground. We found this species in Carolina, where it is rather rare, and also obtained specimens from Georgia."

—Quads. Vol. II, p. 304.

Fig. 128. AUDUBON GRASSHOPPER MOUSE (page 180)

"This pretty little animal was discovered for us in the neighborhood of Fort Union, Missouri, in 1843. It was in full summer pelage. Then being in quest of Antelopes and large animals, we did not give it that close attention which we should have. A glance at our plate will suffice to convince anyone that it is entirely new."

—Quads. Vol. II, p. 328.

Fig. 129 (left). TOWNSEND'S MEADOW MOUSE (page 180)

"The specimen was obtained on July 21, 1835, by J. K. Townsend, on the shores of the Columbia river."

—Quads. Vol. III, p. 210.

Fig. 129 (center). MEADOW VOLE (page 180)

"J. W. Audubon found this Meadow Vole at the Falls of Niagara. We have also frequently found it in northern New York."

—Quads. Vol. III, p. 212.

Fig. 129 (right). SWAMP RICE RAT (page 180)

"In spring this Rat sits on the dams near water, so immovable, so like the surrounding earth in color, that it is seldom noticed until it moves off to its retreat in the banks."

—Quads. Vol. III, p. 215.

Fig. 130. DOUGLAS'S POCKET GOPHER (page 181)

"This species was first obtained by David Douglas near the mouth of the Columbia river. They are numerous in the neighborhood of Fort Vancouver."

—Quads. Vol. III, p. 25.

Fig. 131. SASKATCHEWAN POCKET GOPHER (page 181)

"The specimen from which our figures were made was presented to the Zoological Society of London. It was obtained at Hudson's Bay."

—Quads. Vol. III, p. 45.

Fig. 132. CAMAS POCKET GOPHER (page 181)

"It derives its name from its fondness for the bulbous roots of the quamash or camash plant."

—Quads. Vol. III, p. 199.

Fig. 133. SHAW POCKET GOPHER (page 182)

"During a visit which we made to the Upper Missouri in 1843 we had many opportunities of studying the habits of this species. We kept four alive for several weeks. They tried constantly to escape by gnawing at the floor. They slept on any of the clothing which would keep them warm. These mischievous pets cut the lining of our hunting coat, and gnawed the leather straps of our trunks. Two of them, entering one of our boots and probably not liking the idea of returning the same way, ate a hole at the toes by which they made their exit."

—Quads. Vol. I, pp. 334, 337.

Fig. 134. EASTERN MUSKRAT (page 182)

"You have probably often seen the Muskrat. In our large cities, you may even have seen his skin, and thought it a beautiful fur.

"When we were about seventeen, we resided on our farm, 'Mill Grove,' at the confluence of the Schuylkill river and the Perkiomen creek. Above a mill dam there was an island, and we occasionally saw Muskrats swimming in the channel. We have now in our possession only two drawings of quadrupeds made by us at this early period, one the Otter, the other a Mink. Drawn with colored chalks and crayons, both are now quite rubbed and soiled, like ourselves having suffered somewhat from the hand of time and the jostling we have encountered."

—Quads. Vol. I, pp. 110–111.

Fig. 135. BUSHY-TAILED WOOD RAT (page 182)

"We have never seen this species in a living state. The trappers dread its attacks on their furs more than they would the approach of a Grizzly Bear. The blankets of the sleeping travellers are sometimes cut to pieces by them, and they carry off small articles from the camp of the hunter."

—Quads. Vol. I, p. 224.

Fig. 136. KANGAROO RAT (page 183)

"This species hop about, kangaroo-fashion, and jump pretty far at a leap. When J. W. Audubon's party encamped in the Tulare Valley of California towards evening, these Rats sometimes came smelling and moving about the legs of the mules, like old friends. One frisked gaily about and several times approached John W. Audubon so nearly that he could have seized it. So great was its curiosity that as the party left the spot it seemed half inclined to follow them.

"Our drawing was made from a beautiful specimen in the British Museum, from near Real del Monte, Mexico."

—Quads. Vol. III, pp. 139, 140.

Fig. 137. COTTON RAT (page 183)

"This species has no other note than a low squeak. When captured it is more savage than the Eastern Wood Rat. Once, while seizing one, we were bitten through a finger covered by a buckskin glove. It obtained its name from its supposed habit of making its nest with cotton, but we have more frequently found the nest of leaves and grasses."

—Quads. Vol. I, p. 231.

Fig. 138. BLACK RAT (page 183)

"The character of this species is so notoriously bad that were we to write a volume in its defense we would fail to remove those prejudices everywhere entertained against this thieving cosmopolite. The Black Rat has been transported to every part of the world where men carry on commerce by means of ships.

"We are willing to admit that the Hessian fly was not brought to America in straw from Hanover, but we contend that the Black Rat and the Norway Rat, greater nuisances perhaps than any other animals, were brought to America from the Old World. There are strong evidences of its existence in Persia long before the discovery of America. It is true there were Rats in our country similar to those of Europe, but these have now been proved to be of very different species."

—Quads. Vol. I, pp. 190, 193.

Fig. 139. EASTERN WOOD RAT (page 184)

"The specimens from which we drew the figures on our plate were obtained in South Carolina and preserved alive in cages. They made no attempt to gnaw their way out. They became very gentle, especially one in a separate cage. It was our custom at dark to release it from confinement, upon which it would run around the room in circles, mount the table we were writing at, and always make efforts to open a particular drawer in which we kept some of its choicest food.

"This is a very active Rat, and in ascending trees it exhibits much of the agility of the Squirrel, although we do not recollect having seen it leap from branch to branch in the manner of that genus.

"The very playful character of this species, its cleanly habits, and mild prominent and bright eyes would render it a far more interesting pet than many others that the caprice of man has from time to time induced him to select."

—*Quads. Vol. I, pp. 33, 35–36.*

Fig. 140. BROWN, OR NORWAY, RAT (page 184)

"In vegetable gardens it devours melons, consuming the sweet fruit.

"We have at different times been able to obtain specimens of this species, which seems to have originated in this country, one from Dr. Samuel Wilson of Charleston, and two from the interior of South Carolina. One was presented to us by a cat, another was caught in a trap. It is but too well known in every portion of our country and throughout the world.

"Our old friend Captain Cummings, who in early life made many voyages to the East Indies, relates to us that one of his captains used to have rats caught when on long voyages. He allowed his sailors a glass of grog for every Rat they caught, and used to invite his mates and passengers to partake of them with due hospitality. Our friend, who was a mate, had a great horror of the captain's invitations, for it was sometimes difficult to ascertain in what form the delicate animals would appear, and to avoid eating them. Not having ourselves eaten Rats (as far as we know), we cannot say whether the old India captain's fondness was justified, but

we do think prejudices are entertained against many animals and reptiles that are, after all, pretty good eating."

—*Quads. Vol. II, pp. 23, 27, 28.*

Letter in the Harvard University Collection:

"Mayor's Office.
New York, Aug. 20, 1841.
"Permission is hereby given Mr. Audubon or his son, to shoot Rats at the Battery early in the morning, so as not to expose the inhabitants in the vicinity to danger.

Robert H. Morris, Mayor."

Fig. 141. CANADA PORCUPINE (page 185)

"The Canada Porcupine, of all North American quadrupeds, possesses the strangest peculiarities in its organization and habits, and in its movements it is the most sluggish. But a wise Creator has endowed it with powers by which it can bid defiance to the whole ferine race, the grizzly bear not excepted, by an impervious coat of mail bristling with bayonets.

"We kept a living animal of the kind in a cage in Charleston for six months. It was occasionally let out to enjoy the benefit of a promenade in the garden and became very gentle. When we called to it, holding in our hand a tempting sweet potato or apple, it would turn its head slowly towards us and give us a mild and wistful look, then with stately steps advance and take the fruit from our hand. If it found the door of our study open it would march in and gently approach us, rubbing its sides against our legs, and look up at us as if supplicating for additional delicacies. We frequently plagued it to try its temper, but it never evinced any spirit of resentment by raising its bristles at us. A large ferocious and troublesome mastiff made a dash one morning at an object which proved to be our Porcupine, which swelled up to nearly double its size. As the dog pounced on it, it dealt him such a sidewise lateral blow with its tail as to cause the mastiff to relinquish his hold and howl in agony—his mouth, tongue and nose full of quills. It was two months before he finally recovered.

"A Porcupine that was confined for some time in the garret of a building in Broadway, New York, in which Peale's Museum was formerly kept, made its escape by gnawing a hole in a corner of the garret, got onto the roof, and tumbled into the street. It was brought the next day to the museum for sale as a great curiosity. The man who brought it said that early in the morning he was attracted by a crowd in the Park watching a strange animal no one could catch. He got a basket and captured the beast. The keeper of the museum paid him half a dollar. The Porcupine was returned to his friends. He was now, however, watched more closely."

—*Quads. Vol. I, pp. 280–281, 285.*

Fig. 142. COMMON STAR-NOSED MOLE (page 186)

"The specimen from which our plate was drawn was captured on a moist piece of ground in New Jersey, near New York."

—*Quads. Vol. II, p. 142.*

Fig. 143. BREWER'S MOLE (page 186)

"We were surprised and gratified at finding this new species. The specimen was obtained by Dr. Yale at Martha's Vineyard. We only had one opportunity of seeing this species alive—on a road near the red sulphur springs in Virginia."

—*Quads. Vol. II, pp. 174, 175.*

Fig. 144. OREGON MOLE (page 186)

"We have little doubt that it is the most common Mole on the Pacific side of the North American continent."

—*Quads. Vol. III, p. 219.*

Fig. 145 (left). FLORIDA POCKET GOPHER (page 186)

"It does not remain underground in winter but continues its diggings throughout the year, devouring roots and grasses."

—*Quads. Vol. III, p. 244.*

Letter from John Bachman to Victor G. Audubon, dated "October 20, 1848, Charleston":

"You will recollect I wrote you about the Southern Pouched Rat [Florida Pocket Gopher]. I will send you a living one. I have had it all summer. It is a gentle and most pleasant companion, eating from my hand and looking at and seeming to talk with me. If John can't figure the one you have already, he must try his hand on this, but don't kill my pet if you can avoid it. I take it out by the tail and hold it in my hand. It has never attempted to bite."

Fig. 145 (center). SHORT-TAILED SHREW (page 186)

"A gardener caught for us the specimens described, at our home, 'Minnie's Land' near New York."

—*Quads. Vol. III, p. 247.*

Fig. 145 (right). CAROLINA SHREW (page 186)

"While we were at the house of Major Lee in Colleton district, South Carolina, his huntsman brought in some wild Ducks, and also a hooded Merganser with a protuberance in its throat. It had not fully swallowed some food when it was shot. Opening the throat we found this little Shrew, fresh and perfect."

—*Quads. Vol. III, p. 250.*

Fig. 145 (right foreground). COMMON MOLE OR PRAIRIE MOLE (page 186)

"Our figure and description were made from a beautifully furred Mole found by Dr. George C. Leib in the Michigan prairies."

—*Quads. Vol. III, p. 253.*

Fig. 146. COMMON MOLE (page 187)

"We kept one of this species alive, feeding it altogether on earth-worms. We were much interested in observing that no matter how soiled its coat might have become in the cage, it would resume its beauty and glossiness after the mole had passed and re-passed through the earth eight or ten times. Its great strength enabled it to lift the lid of the box in which it was kept. We put the Mole into a large wire rat-trap, and to our surprise saw him insert his forepaws between the wires and force them apart sufficiently to give him room to pass out through them.

"The idea that Moles have no eyes is an error. They would find a large pair of eyes one of the greatest evils, inasmuch as they would be filled with sand, causing inflammation and blindness.

"We preserved one in a cage in Carolina during winter to ascertain whether it would become dormant. Until the middle of January it ran actively through the moist earth in which we placed worms, then it seemed to have gone to winter quarters. We examined every part of the room without success. The cage of the Mole had been set on a box full of earth, in which the chrysalides of some sixty or seventy species of rare butterflies, moths, and 'sphinges' had been carefully deposited. In this box a few days later we heard a noise, and on looking we discovered our little fugitive. He had devoured our choice insects, putting an end to all our hopes of reading a better lesson on entomology the following spring than ever could have been taught us."

—*Quads. Vol. I, pp. 84–85, 89–90.*

Fig. 147. CAROLINA SHORT-TAILED SHREW (*page 188*)

"Living beneath the surface of the earth, this little quadruped feeds on worms and the larvae of insects, shunning the light, and restricted to a little world of its own, best suited to its habits and enjoyments."

—*Quads. Vol. II, p. 177.*

Fig. 148. WATER SHREW (*page 188*)

"These animals are so minute in the scale of quadrupeds that they will always be overlooked unless sought with zeal, and even then it is difficult to meet with or procure them alive. Our drawing was made from a specimen in the British Museum, London."

—*Quads. Vol. III, p. 109.*

Fig. 149. LITTLE SHORT-TAILED SHREW (*page 188*)

"This little creature was first captured by Titian R. Peale (during Long's Expedition to the Rocky Mountains) at Engineer Cantonment on the Missouri. It was found in a pitfall excavated for catching Wolves. Look at the plate, reader, and imagine the astonishment of the hunter when, instead of the savage prowlers of the prairies that he intended to entrap, he saw this smallest of our mammals running across the bottom."

—*Quads. Vol. II, p. 147.*

Fig. 150. VIRGINIA OPOSSUM (*page 189*)

"We can imagine to ourselves the surprise with which the Opossum was regarded by Europeans when they first saw it in our country. Here was a strange animal with the head and ears of a pig, sometimes hanging on a limb, and occasionally swinging like a monkey by the tail! Around that prehensile appendage a dozen sharp-nosed, sleek-headed young had entwined their own tails and were sitting on the mother's back. The astonished traveller approaches this extraordinary compound of an animal and touches it cautiously with a stick. Its eyes close, it falls to the ground, it ceases to move, and appears to be dead! He turns it on its back, and perceives in its stomach a strange apparently artificial opening, a pocket with another brood of a dozen or more young, each scarcely larger than a pea, hanging in clusters on the teats. The twinkling of the half-closed eye and the breathing of the creature show that it is not dead, and the traveller adds a new term to his language, that of 'playing 'possum.' The habit of feigning death to deceive an enemy is common to several species of quadrupeds, such as the common Red Fox, but in none is it more artfully exhibited than in the Opossum.

"It has scarcely any note of recognition, and but for a low growl when molested it is remarkably silent. It displays no cunning in avoiding traps. From its very prolific nature it can afford to have many enemies—men and dogs, the Great Horned Owl, the White-headed Eagle, the Wolf, and the Rattlesnake."

—*Quads. Vol. II, pp. 109–110, 116.*

Fig. 151 (top figure). BLACK FOX SQUIRREL (page 190)

"This Squirrel was first described by John Bachman from a specimen obtained by J. W. Audubon in Louisiana."

—*Quads. Vol. III, p. 261.*

Fig. 151 (lower figure). RED-BELLIED SQUIRREL (page 190)

"Our specimen came from California. It nests in the oaks or nut-bearing pines, where it hides itself among the evergreen foliage when alarmed. Except when surprised on the ground or near the earth it can seldom be killed."

—*Quads. Vol. III, p. 259.*

Fig. 152 (left). HARRIS'S ANTELOPE GROUND SQUIRREL (page 191)

"Mr. Townsend gave the specimen to our esteemed friend Edward Harris, from whom we received it, and with whose name we have honored this pretty little animal from the West."

—*Quads. Vol. III, p. 268.*

Fig. 152 (right). CALIFORNIA VOLE (page 191)

"We present our thanks to Major Le Conte for the loan of the skin from which our figure was drawn."

—*Quads. Vol. III, p. 271.*

Fig. 153 (right). COLONEL ABERT'S SQUIRREL (page 191)

"It gives us great pleasure to welcome this beautiful new animal under the name of Colonel Abert's Squirrel. Dr. Woodhouse remarks: 'This beautiful Squirrel I procured whilst attached to the expedition under command of Captain L. Sitgreaves, Topographical Engineer, U. S. Army, exploring the Zuñi and the great and little Colorado rivers of the West in October, 1851, in the San Francisco Mountains, New Mexico.' "

—*Quads. Vol. III, p. 263.*

Fig. 153 (left). WESTERN, OR CALIFORNIA, GRAY SQUIRREL (page 191)

"This Squirrel has often been killed in the California pine woods near Murphy's 'diggings.' "

—*Quads. Vol. III, p. 265.*

Fig. 154. LONG-TAILED RED FOX (page 192)

"This animal was first noticed by Lewis and Clark as the large Fox of the plains. We obtained a beautiful specimen from Captain Rhett of the U. S. Army, who found it in Utah, near Fort Laramie. Its habits are similar to those of the Red Fox. It runs into many varieties of color."

—*Quads. Vol. III, p. 256.*

Fig. 155. CRAB-EATING RACCOON (page 192)

"This Raccoon conceals itself by day in the California oak trees. Its food consists of acorns, grapes, berries, eggs, birds and chickens. It is often seen near the water courses, being fond of frogs, fish and crabs. It is probably most abundant within the tropics.

"The figure given in our plate was made by J. W. Audubon in the British Museum, from one procured in Mexico or California."

—*Quads. Vol. III, pp. 273, 274.*

Fig. 156. AMERICAN MINK (page 192)

See note for figure 34 on page 75.

PRESENT LOCATION OF KNOWN ORIGINAL STUDIES FOR "THE QUADRUPEDS"

	Plate No. in The Quadrupeds	Figure No. in Audubon's Animals
Northern Flying Squirrel; Richardardson's Flying Squirrel ("Severn River Flying Squirrel"; "Rocky Mountain Flying Squirrel")	CXLIII	94
Fremont's Chickaree; Black Fox Squirrel ("Fremont's Squirrel"; "Sooty Squirrel")	CXLIX	83

MORRIS TYLER, WOODBRIDGE, CONNECTICUT
Water color by J. J. Audubon:

Marsh Rabbit ("Carolina Swamp Rabbit")	XVIII	65
Oils by J. W. Audubon:		
Columbia Black-tailed Deer	CVI	49
Say's Mantled Ground Squirrel ("Say's Marmot Squirrel")	CXIV	99
Texas Jack "Rabbit" ("Texan Hare")	CXXXIII	68

MISS MARJORIE BOULTON, ST. LOUIS, MISSOURI
Water color by J. J. Audubon:

Flying Squirrel, similar to Plate XXVIII		92

JOHN S. WILLIAMS, NEW YORK
Water color by J. J. Audubon:

Say's Chipmunk ("Four-striped Ground Squirrel") (On deposit at Princeton University)		96

(two companion studies for Plate XXIV)

THOMAS J. GANNON, INC., NEW YORK
Water color by J. J. Audubon:

Swamp Rabbit ("Swamp Hare")	XXXVII	64

MRS. MARGARET MC CORMICK, TOTTENVILLE, NEW YORK
Oils by J. W. Audubon:

Mexican Ground Squirrel	CIX	103

(Plates of folio CIX and CXXIV were merged to form only CIX in octavo.)

Mexican Rock Squirrel	CXXXIX	104
Grizzly Bear (rear figure only)	CXXXI	21
California Gray Squirrel	CLIII	153

(one of two oils combined for octavo Plate CLIII)

HENRY E. SCHNAKENBERG, NEWTOWN, CONNECTICUT
Three water color companion studies by J. J. Audubon, and one oil possibly by Victor G. Audubon for:

Redwood Chickaree or Red Squirrel ("Soft-haired Squirrel")	XIX	87

EDWIN HEWITT GALLERY, NEW YORK
Water color by J. J. Audubon:

Cross Fox	VI	16

BOATMEN'S NATIONAL BANK, ST. LOUIS, MISSOURI
Water color by J. J. Audubon:

Western Fox Squirrel ("Say's Squirrel")	LXXXIX	80

HENRY L. SAVAGE, PRINCETON, NEW JERSEY
Oil by J. W. Audubon:

Armadillo	CXLVI	43

	Plate No. in The Quadrupeds	Figure No. in Audubon's Animals

MISS SUSAN LEWIS SHAFFER, CINCINNATI, OHIO
Oil by J. W. Audubon:

Ring-tailed Cat ("Ring-tailed Bassaris")	XCVIII	25

MUSEUM OF COMPARATIVE ZOOLOGY, HARVARD UNIVERSITY
Water color by J. J. Audubon:

Meadow Jumping Mouse ("Jumping Mouse")	LXXXV	122

MRS. C. F. WOLTERS, SWARTHMORE, PENNSYLVANIA
Oil by J. J. Audubon:

Canada Otter (also titled: "Entrapped Otter")	LI	36

THE OLD PRINT SHOP, INC., NEW YORK
Oils by J. W. Audubon (two double oils, with studies for four plates):

Richardson's Vole; Drummond's Vole ("Richardson's Meadow Mouse"; "Drummond's Meadow Mouse")	CXXXV	116
Richardson's Lemming ("Northern Meadow Mouse")	CXXIX	119
Tawny Lemming; American Lemming ("Tawny Lemming"; "Back's Lemming")	CXX	120
Collared Lemming ("Hudson's Bay Lemming")	CXIX	121

KNOEDLER ART GALLERIES, NEW YORK
Water color by J. J. Audubon:

Muskrat (sold to anonymous collector)	XIII	134
Oil by J. W. Audubon:		
Colonel Abert's Squirrel (sold to anonymous dealer)	CLIII	153

(octavo only)

NATIONAL GALLERY OF ART, WASHINGTON, D. C.
Oils by J. J. Audubon (recently found in Australia and presented by E. J. L. Hallstrom of Sydney):

Arctic Hare ("Polar Hare")	XXXII	62

(The plate shows one of the two hares only—hare in summer pelage.)

New York Weasel ("White Weasel")	LIX	33

Oils by J. W. Audubon (also presented this year, after discovery in Australia):

Long-tailed Red Fox ("Jackall Fox")	CLI	154
Black-footed Ferret	XCIII	26

NATIONAL AUDUBON SOCIETY, NEW YORK
Oil by J. W. Audubon:

Bonaparte Weasel ("Tawny Weasel")	CXLVIII	30

KENNEDY & COMPANY, NEW YORK
Oil by J. W. Audubon:

Saskatchewan Pocket Gopher ("Mole-shaped Pouched Rat")	CX	131

CITY ART MUSEUM OF ST. LOUIS, MISSOURI
Water color by J. J. Audubon:

Texas Jack "Rabbit"	LXIII	69

BIBLIOGRAPHY

Limitations of space prohibit listing all the many references consulted for this study. Readers in search of a virtually definitive biography are referred to F. H. Herrick's *Audubon the Naturalist*, 1938 edition.

For collectors: Herrick's bibliography of "The Quadrupeds," as published in *The Auk*, vol. 36, 1919, pp. 372–380 (with additional data):

Audubon, John James, and Bachman, The Rev. John. *The Viviparous Quadrupeds of North America*. 3 vols. 150 lithographic colored plates. Imperial folio. Published by J. J. Audubon. New York, 1845–1848. Vol. I, parts 1–10, pls. 1–50, 1845. Vol. II, parts 11–20, pls. 51–100, 1846. Vol. III, parts 21–30, pls. 101–150, 1848.

Issued to subscribers in 30 parts of 5 plates each, size 28 x 22 inches, to compose 3 vols. (though sometimes bound in 2 vols. with one title omitted), at $10 a part, or $300, without text except titles, table of contents, and names on plates. [See page 58 for number of pictures done by J. J. Audubon and by J. W. Audubon.] Author's and printer's legends read: "Drawn from Nature by J. J. Audubon, F.R.S.F.L.S.," and "Lith. Printed & Cold. by J. T. Bowen, Phila."

Audubon, John James, and Bachman, Rev. John. *The Viviparous Quadrupeds of North America*. 3 vols. Royal octavo. Published by J. J. Audubon and V. G. Audubon. New York and London (in part), 1846–1853. First edition, without plates, issued to subscribers to the Imperial folio edition, as above. Vol. I, pp. i–xvi, 1–390; published by J. J. Audubon, New York. Vol. II, pp. 1–336; published by V. G. Audubon, New York, 1851. Vol. III, pp. i–vi, 1–257; published by V. G. Audubon, New York, 1853. (Vol. I was also published in London by Wiley & Putnam in 1847.)

A supplement of 93 pages and 5 colored plates, added in 1854, and apparently issued to all previous subscribers to this and the large folio, is sometimes bound up with the third volume of the present edition, with the date usually quoted as "1854."

Audubon, John James, and Bachman, The Rev. John. *The Quadrupeds of North America*. 3 vols. Royal octavo. 155 lithographic colored plates. Published by V. G. Audubon. New York, 1849–1854. Vol. I, nos. 1–10, pp. i–viii, 1–383; 1849. Vol. II, nos. 11–20, pp. 1–334; 1851. Vol. III, nos. 21–31, pp. iii–v, 1–348; 1854.

First octavo edition of text and plates, issued to subscribers in 31 parts (in printed covers) of 5 plates each, at $1.00 a part, the number of plates being reduced to 155 by the omission of one of the small plates in the supplement mentioned under Royal octavo edition above. A set in the original (unbound) paper-covered parts was quoted by Samuel N. Rhoads in his catalogue (No. 39) on "Auduboniana and Other Nature Books," 1919.

Same as preceding. Second octavo edition of text and plates. 1854.

Same as preceding. Third and, so far as is known, last octavo edition with text and plates. 1856.

Note: All plates in the first octavo edition were lithographed by J. T. Bowen except for seventeen in Vol. I: "Printed by Nagel & Weingaertner, New York." The name of the artist who drew the Audubon pictures on stone is usually shown beneath each plate: W. E. Hitchcock for Bowen; R. Trembly for Nagel & Weingaertner; Trembly drew one plate for Bowen, the Mink in plate 33. According to Stanley Clisby Arthur, a fourth octavo edition was printed in 1860.

BIOGRAPHIES

Arthur, Stanley Clisby. *Audubon, an Intimate Life of the American Woodsman*. New Orleans, 1937. An authoritative biography which adds much new material to Herrick's writings, particularly on Audubon in the South.

Audubon, John James. *Ornithological Biography*. 5 vols. Royal 8vo. Edinburgh, 1831–1839. Source of Audubon's account of the destruction of his drawings by Norway Rats.

Audubon, Lucy, ed. *The Life of John James Audubon, the Naturalist*. New York, 1869.

Audubon, Maria R. "Audubon's Story of his Youth." *Scribner's Magazine*, vol. XIII, pp. 267–287, illus. New York, 1893. Audubon's sketch of his life, "Myself, J. J. Audubon." Repeated in *Audubon and His Journals*.

Brannon, Peter A. *Edward Harris, Friend of Audubon.* New York, 1947.

Burroughs, John. *John James Audubon.* Boston, 1902.

Dall, W. H. *Spencer Fullerton Baird, a Biography, including Selections from his correspondence with Audubon.* Philadelphia, 1915.

Godwin, Parke. "John James Audubon." In *The Homes of American Authors.* New York, 1853.

Herrick, Francis Hobart. *Audubon, the Naturalist, A History of His Life and Time.* 2 vols. New York, 1917. (Revised and published in one volume, 1938, with a final disputation of the Lost Dauphin legend of Audubon's birth, and additions to the Bibliography.) The most comprehensive and authoritative biography; with S. C. Arthur recommended as collateral reading.

Rose, Jennie Haskell. *John Bachman at Home.* Charleston Museum Ms., n.d.

Rourke, Constance. *Audubon.* New York, 1936. A popular fictional life.

Speed, John Gilmer. *John Bachman.* Charleston, 1888. The only available life of Bachman, it is an overedited and distorted version of the Bachman letters in the Charleston Museum.

Webber, C. W. *Romance of Forest and Prairie Life.* London, 1853.

JOURNALS and LETTERS

Audubon, John James. Unpublished letters. Princeton University; National Audubon Society; Library Company of Philadelphia; Museum of Comparative Zoology, Harvard University; American Philosophical Society, Philadelphia; New York Public Library.

Audubon, John Woodhouse. *Audubon's Western Journal: 1849–1850, Being the Ms. of a trip from New York to Texas, and an overland journey through Mexico and Arizona to the gold-fields of California.* Cleveland, 1906. A Journal by J. W. Audubon, with a biographical memoir by his daughter, Maria R. Audubon.

Audubon, John Woodhouse. *Illustrated Notes of an Expedition Through Mexico and California.* New York, 1852. A rare book with four color plates.

Audubon, Maria R. *Audubon and His Journals,* with zoological and other notes by Elliott Coues. 2 vols. New York, 1897. Besides containing the European, Labrador, and Missouri River Journals of Audubon, this important work contains a biography of, and an autobiography by, J. J. Audubon.

Bachman, the Reverend John. Unpublished Letters. The Charleston Museum, Charleston, South Carolina. (The collection also includes letters from Victor G. Audubon to Bachman, and others.)

Brannon, Peter A. *Edward Harris, Friend of Audubon.* New York, 1947.

Corning, Howard, ed. *Journal made while obtaining subscriptions to his "Birds of America,"* 1840–43. Cambridge, The Business Historical Society, 1929.

Corning, Howard, ed. *Journal of John James Audubon made during his trip to New Orleans in 1820–21.* Boston, The Club of Odd Volumes, 1929.

Corning, Howard, ed. *Letters of John James Audubon, 1826–1840.* 2 vols. Boston, The Club of Odd Volumes, 1930.

Harris, Edward. *Journal and Diary of the Missouri River Expedition.* Original ms. in the Department of Archives and History, the State of Alabama, Montgomery; copy in the Library of the Philadelphia Academy of Sciences. To be published by the University of St. Louis; Dr. J. F. McDermott, editor.

Peattie, Donald Culross, ed. *Audubon's America.* New York, 1940. A popular work based on Audubon's journals and episodes.

POPULAR REFERENCES

Anthony, H. E. *Field Book of North American Mammals.* New York, 1928.

Anthony, H. E., and others. *Animals of the World.* Garden City, 1947.

Cahalane, Victor. *Mammals of North America.* New York, 1947.

Hamilton, W. J., Jr. *American Mammals.* New York, 1939.

Hamilton, W. J., Jr. *The Mammals of the Eastern United States.* Ithaca, 1943.

EXHIBITION CATALOGUES

The Academy of Natural Sciences, Philadelphia. *John J. Audubon, a National Exhibition.* April 26–June 1, 1938. 40 pages.

Princeton University Library. *An Audubon Anthology of Drawings, Prints, Plates, Books, and Manuscripts.* November 9–December 9, 1950. Notes by H. C. Rice, Jr.

National Audubon Society, New York. Three Centennial Exhibitions: Winter, Spring, Fall, 1951.

INDEX

Entries printed in SMALL CAPITALS refer to illustrations.

BULL, 38

CACOMISTLE, 101
CARIBOU, BARREN GROUND, 122
Cartwright, Captain:
  journal of, 77
CAT:
  CIVET, 101
  LEOPARD, 79
  MOUNTAIN, 101
  RING-TAILED, 101
  SPOTTED, 79
  TIGER, 79
CATAMOUNT, 84, 85
Catlin, George, 32
Chamois, European, 197
Chardon, 70
CHICKAREE, 157
  DOUGLAS's, 158, 159
  FREMONT's, 152
  REDWOOD, 156
CHIPMUNK:
  EASTERN, 164
  SAY's, 165
  TOWNSEND's, 166
Chouteau, Auguste, 29
Chouteau, Pierre, 29
Clark, William, see Lewis, Meriwether, and Clark, William
Clavigero, Francisco J., 199
Collie, 202
Constant, 23
CONY, 132
Cottontail Rabbit, 27
Coues, Elliott, 18
COUGAR, 84, 85
Council Bluffs, 32–33
COYOTE, 86
Culbertson, Alexander, 43, 45, 73
  Audubon's portrait of, 46
Cummings, Samuel, Captain, 18, 211

Daubigny, Charles, Dr., 18
daughters, Audubon's, 17
David, Jacques Louis, instructor of
  Audubon, 17, 23
DEER, 35, 36
  COLUMBIA BLACK-TAILED, 120
  MULE, 118
  OREGON WHITE-TAILED, 119
  VIRGINIA, 116, 117
  WHITE-TAILED, 116, 117
DEER, HEAD OF A, 35
Derby, Earl of, 193
diary of the return voyage (Audubon's), 48–56
"Doe, Head of a," 45

DOE, HEAD OF A, 37
DOG:
  ESKIMO, 52, 90
  HARE INDIAN, 89
DOGS, 38
Douglas, David, 203, 209

"Eagle and Lamb," 22, 23
EAGLE AND LAMB, 39
Edinburgh Society of Arts, Audubon
  elected to, 20
ELK, AMERICAN, 121
Episodes of Western Life, 58
ERMINE, 104
expedition, Upper Missouri river:
  Audubon's description of animals
    seen on, 42, 48, 53, 54, 55, 56
  few remaining sketches from, 45

FERRET, BLACK-FOOTED, 102
FISHER, 103
Fort Clark, 43
Fort George, 41
Fort Pierre, 41, 42
Fort Union, 43–48
Fox, Black (Silver Fox), 69
FOX:
  ARCTIC, 95
  BLUE, 95
  CROSS, 92
  GRAY, 94
  KIT, 93
  LONG-TAILED RED, 192
  RED, 92
  SILVER, 91
  SWIFT, 93
  WHITE, 95
FOX AND GOOSE, 39
"Fox and Pheasants," 20, 21
Franklin, Sir John, 208
Fremont, John Charles, Colonel, 202

Gérard, 23
Gilliard, E. Thomas, opinion of, on
  Audubon's oils, 18
Gilman, John, Reverend, 24
glazing, Audubon's opinion of, 21
GOAT, ROCKY MOUNTAIN, 126
Goats, Wild (Rocky Mountain Bighorn), 197
Godman, John Davidson, 70
Godwin, Parke, 27
GOPHER:
  CAMAS POCKET, 181
  DOUGLAS's POCKET, 181
  FLORIDA POCKET, 186
  SASKATCHEWAN POCKET, 181

GOPHER (cont.):
  SHAW POCKET, 182
Gregg, William, 22

Hall, Basil, 21
HARE:
  AMERICAN, 34, 130, 131
  ARCTIC, 51, 132
  LITTLE CHIEF, 132
  PRAIRIE, 136
  SNOWSHOE, 130, 131
  TAILLESS, 132
  VARYING, 130, 131
  WHISTLING, 132
  WHITE, 130, 131
Harris, Edward, 28, 29, 214
Havell, Robert, 24
HEAD OF A BUFFALO CALF, 40
HEAD OF A DEER, 35
HEAD OF A DOE, 37
Henderson, Ky., 17, 18
Hernandez, Dr., 199
Herriott, 200
Hondecoeter, Melchior d', Audubon's
  opinion of, 21
HORSES, 38
horses, wild, 69
Houston, General Sam, 67
Hudson's Bay Fur Company, 69, 197, 202, 208

Illingsworth, 41
Indians:
  Audubon's opinion of, 32, 43
  Audubon shows drawings to, 31

JAGUAR, 83
Jardine, Sir William, 20

KALAN, 109

Landseeer, Edwin Henry, Audubon's
  opinion of, 21–22
Lawrence, Sir Thomas, 23
Le Conte, Major, 214
"Le Conte's Mouse" (see also VOLE, PINE), 59
Lee, Major, 212
Lehman, George, 23
Leib, George C., Dr., 212
Leitner, Dr., 208
LEMMING:
  AMERICAN, 177
  COLLARED, 178
  RICHARDSON's, 177
  TAWNY, 177
Lewis, Meriwether, and Clark, William, 30, 195, 197, 206, 214

Entries printed in SMALL CAPITALS refer to illustrations.

Entries printed in SMALL CAPITALS refer to illustrations.

Entries printed in SMALL CAPITALS refer to illustrations.